Dr Patricia Carrington, the originator of CSM, is a clinical psychologist specializing in stress management. For eleven years a lecturer in the Department of Psychology at Princeton University, she is presently Associate Clinical Professor of Psychiatry at UMDNJ/Robert Wood Johnson Medical School. She has long been involved with meditation both personally as a regular meditator and professionally, using meditation with her patients and conducting research in this area.

Since she developed her own technique of meditation, Clinically Standardized Meditation, this method has been used successfully by numerous organizations and by individuals in all walks of life who wish to reduce stress and enhance the quality of their lives. As Administrative Consultant to the Employee Health Maintenance Programme at New York Telephone Company, she has assisted this company's medical department to institute one of the largest, most successful, stress management programmes ever undertaken by a major corporation.

Dr Carrington's book *Freedom In Meditation*, has been translated into several languages and was recognised as the major work to date on the clinical use of meditation. Now substantially revised and re-titled *The Book of Meditation* (Element Books, 1998), this book is the companion volume to the *Learn to Meditate* kit. Her other book, *Releasing* (William Morrow, 1984) has been hailed as a breakthrough in the field of stress management.

At present Dr Carrington divides her professional time between her work with patients, teaching, research and writing. At home she finds time to enjoy a quiet Japanese garden.

by the same author

The Book of Meditation
the companion volume to the *Learn to Meditate kit*

Acknowledgements:
Dr Herbert Benson of Harvard Medical School, Dr Robert Woolfolk of Rutgers University and Dr Bradford Wilson have generously granted permission to include descriptions of their respective breathing meditation methods in the CSM workbook, thereby extending the scope and flexibility of the teaching method.

Learn to MEDITATE

THE COMPLETE COURSE IN MODERN MEDITATION

Patricia Carrington PhD

Foreword by
Dr Michael Weir

ELEMENT

Shaftesbury, Dorset • Boston, Massachusetts
Melbourne, Victoria

Revised edition first published in Great Britain in 1995 by Learning for Life Ltd

Second revised edition first published in Great Britain in 1998 by
Element Books Limited
Shaftesbury, Dorset SP7 8BP

Published in the USA in 1998 by
Element Books, Inc.
160 North Washington Street , Boston, MA 02114

Published in Australia in 1998 by
Element Books and distributed
by Penguin Australia Ltd
487 Maroondah Highway, Ringwood,
Victoria 3134

This edition of the text has been revised by Richard Berg FCA
(UKRC Registered Independent Counsellor)

Reprinted 1998 and 1999

Cover design by Slatter-Anderson
Design by Roger Lightfoot
Typeset by Bournemouth Colour Press
Printed and bound in Hong Kong by Dai Nippon

British Library Cataloguing in Publication
data available

Library of Congress Cataloging in Publication
data available

ISBN 1 86204 191 1

Foreword
by Dr Michael Weir

Modern programmes of preventive medicine and health promotion are increasingly recognizing the contribution of stress to health breakdown and disease progression. Given the pervasive nature of stressful demands neither their avoidance or eradication are possible. To survive and prosper in a world of escalating demands it is essential therefore that we develop personal resilience and appropriate stress management strategies.

Clinically Standardized Meditation (CSM) is a carefully researched and highly effective method for stress reduction which gives individuals the stress management skills and insight that modern life requires. Over the past 12 years I have employed the technique with many hundreds of individuals in programmes of rehabilitation and occupational medicine. Patients recovering from heart attacks and cancer as well as high flying executives have derived major benefits from the regular practice of CSM. Benefits which have emerged from its practice have included a host of physical and psychological gains. Greater work satisfaction, improved relationships and more harmonious home lives have regularly been reported.

The technique is rewarding to practice and significant benefits are apt to be realized quite soon after its regular practice has commenced. My researches indicate that its employment in the longer term can help to address the psychological and physiological factors which compromize the immune system and underpin many forms of addiction.

My experience of the benefits of CSM in many settings allows me to unreservedly recommend this major stress management technique to anyone interested in improving his or her health and well-being.

Michael Weir, MB ChB,
Member of the Faculty of Public Health Medicine of the Royal College of Physicians (London)
Former Director of Community and Occupational Medicine, Wirral Health Authorty

How this course works

The CSM Self-Regulated Course consists of:

1 an instruction workbook, which you are now reading
2 four one-hour cassette tapes created and narrated by Dr Patricia Carrington.

To learn CSM you will use the workbook and tapes in a coordinated fashion.

The course is divided into essential and optional material.

1	**Essential Reading:**	These sections must be read. They are highlighted by shading in the Programme (on pages vii–xi and in the text.
2	**Optional Reading:**	This consists of additional information, questionnaires, advisory sheets and other material; all are highly recommended but are not essential to your learning of meditation.
3	**Audio Tapes:**	Listen to Sides 1 to 6 when indicated. They are essential to your learning of meditation and are highlighted by shading in the Programme. Sides 7 and 8 are optional but will be valuable for many people.

The Programme starting on the next page tells you exactly what to do.

YOUR PROGRAMME FOR THIS COURSE

It is important to work through the course in programme order. See previous page for an explanation of shaded items.

Section 1 INTRODUCTION

What to Read or Do	Page
Special Considerations	1
Using This Workbook	3
Introduction to CSM	4
Listen to Introductory Talk – Sides 1 and 2	Tape

Section 2 PREPARING FOR MEDITATION

What to Read or Do	Page
Steps 1 to 7	6
Selecting Your Special Sound (Mantra)	10
Room Preparations	12

Section 3 LEARNING TO MEDITATE

Section 4 HELPING MEDITATION WORK

This workbook is also a reference volume containing information you may need in the future. By using the index you can locate advice about handling most of the problems that a modern meditator is likely to face. There are page numbers and also references to the recordings.

Section 1

INTRODUCTION

Special Considerations

If you suffer from depression, phobias, drug dependence, or other psychiatric symptoms

While meditation is helpful in relieving stress, it is not a form of psychiatric treatment. If you have severe emotional problems you should undertake meditation only under the supervision of a qualified professional in the mental health field: a psychiatrist, psychologist, or other mental health practitioner who can advise you about coordinating meditation with your on-going treatment. A detailed discussion on how to use meditation as an adjunct to psychotherapy is contained in the CSM Instructor's Kit available to health professionals,[1] and in *The Book of Meditation* (the companion volume to the *Learn to Meditate* kit).

If you suffer from a physical illness

If you are undertaking meditation with the intention of alleviating a physical condition related to stress, discuss

[1]Available from Learning for Life Ltd – see page 100 for details.

this first with your doctor and remain under his or her supervision. **You should continue with your medical care even if your physical condition appears to be improving** – only your doctor can judge whether it is actually improving. In addition, there are certain physical illnesses (for example, high blood pressure and diabetes) in which the required dosage of medicine may change after starting meditation and it is essential that a doctor monitors your condition. **Before you start your meditation programme ask your doctor to read** 'Information Sheet for Doctors' **on pages 84–8 of this workbook – it contains information expressly designed for doctors whose patients practise CSM.**

If you are under 12 years of age

The method of meditation taught here is not suitable for most children under 12 years of age because it requires sitting still most of the time. There are, however, some 'moving' forms of meditation for children that are taught by reliable meditation organizations. You might want to learn one of these. If not, it is best to postpone learning meditation.

If you are a teenager who wants to learn meditation

You will be able to learn very satisfactorily providing you follow the directions on page 36 for adjusting your meditation time to suit your age. Your maximum meditation time should not ordinarily exceed (in minutes) the number of years of your age. For example, 14-year-olds do not usually find it suitable to meditate for more than 14 minutes during any one session.

If you are a couple who wants to learn meditation (or a member of a group)

It is not advisable to use the actual instruction recording (Side 3) with more than one person at a time since it is designed for individual use only. Without a very experienced meditation teacher who is prepared to handle all contingencies, the least noise made by any person who is learning, such as coughing, giggling, or talking spontaneously, can seriously disrupt the learning of the other group members and may spoil the effectiveness of the recording for them, now and in the future.

Each person should therefore listen to the Instruction Session (Side 3) when alone. Later a group or couple may listen jointly to the remaining sessions (Sides 4, 5, 6, 7 and 8). They may also start by listening together to the Introductory Talk (Sides 1 and 2). **Each member of a group (or couple) will need a workbook of their own**. After becoming experienced at meditating, a group (or couple) can meditate together whenever they wish to do so. Group meditation is a very special experience and can be highly satisfactory.

Using This Workbook

This Workbook Can Be Used in Three Different Ways

1 It gives essential instructions to accompany the recordings. These instructions take up a small part of the workbook and can be read quickly. The remainder of the workbook contains useful information which is highly recommended but not essential to your learning of meditation. If your meditation is going smoothly with no problems, you may decide to confine your reading to the essential instructions only. For your convenience, the essential instructions that you *must* read when learning are separated from those that you *can* read for additional information or for future reference. **Essential instructions are highlighted with shading**.

2 It contains programmed instruction materials consisting of a series of questionnaires and accompanying advisory sheets. Using these materials has been found to be extremely helpful to those learning meditation, but if you would rather not fill out questionnaires, omit them. You can learn to meditate from the recordings alone plus the essential instructions mentioned in 1 above.

3 This workbook is also a reference volume containing information you may need in the future. By using the index in the back you can locate advice about handling most of the problems that a modern meditator is likely to face. By consulting it, you will quickly be able to turn to specific charts, advisory sheets, or recordings whenever you need to.

Introduction to Clinically Standardized Meditation

You will be learning Clinically Standardized Meditation (or CSM), a leading relaxation technique. CSM is particularly easy to learn because it does not require conscious effort or concentration. Those practising it often report that they feel their meditation sessions to be a break from everyday pressures and that after meditating they find they are more relaxed and capable of handling problems more easily. Regular CSM meditators have variously reported a lessening of a sense of urgency in life, an easing of tensions, lowered anxiety, less irritability, greater energy and productivity, increased clarity of thought, and more restful sleep – among other benefits.

It is important for those who are planning to learn CSM to realize that this method differs from other forms of meditation in that it is self-regulated. As you go through the basic steps of learning, you will find out how to adjust your own meditation, so that it suits your personal needs. CSM is easily mastered over a period of nine days. All the instructions necessary to learn and practise it satisfactorily are contained in this workbook and the accompanying audio cassettes.

Note

Throughout this workbook you will notice what may seem to you to be a rather inconsistent and improper use of the pronouns 'they', 'them', and 'their'. To avoid gender-linked pronouns, I have used these personal pronouns not only to represent the plural, but also either sex in the singular.

NOW LISTEN TO INTRODUCTORY TALK – SIDES 1 and 2

Section 2

PREPARING FOR MEDITATION

You will need to make a few simple arrangements before setting out to learn meditation.

Step One

If you have not already listened to your tapes Sides 1 and 2, they can be played as soon as you wish. They contain an introductory talk by Dr Patricia Carrington (originator of CSM) talking about some of the benefits you may obtain from meditation and how to prepare for your first instruction session. *Play these two sides **before** you learn meditation.*

Step Two

Side 3 of the tapes is your instruction session. It should not be played until you have arranged to be alone and uninterrupted for one full hour. Be sure to read Section 2 of this workbook before playing the recording, so that you can make the necessary preparations for learning. Sides 4, 5, 6, 7 and 8 will be played later at intervals, according to directions.

Step Three

Many people find it useful to plan to learn meditation over a weekend because a Saturday–Sunday time-slot allows ample time for the instruction session and the follow-up session the next day – but any block of time when you can schedule an hour to yourself on each of two consecutive days is fine.

Step Four

You should not be interrupted during your instruction session. To avoid this make certain that other members of your household (dormitory, etc) will be out of the building or that they will be quiet during this time.

If they have to be within your hearing distance, they should understand that it is essential that you are not interrupted when you are learning meditation. Request that they do not play the radio, TV, or music, and that they do not shout or talk loudly during this special hour. It may help if you explain that you will not always ask this complete silence of them when you are meditating. It is only your first lesson that must be entirely free of distractions.

Step Five

You will need to make some preparations involving your physical and mental state when learning meditation. Instruction in meditation should be undertaken when you are alert and rested. Therefore:

1 You should not take any alcoholic beverages or non-prescription drugs that alter your state of consciousness **for at least 24 hours** before your instruction in meditation. Meditation requires clear-headedness, so you should not meditate while under the influence of alcohol or any non-prescription, mind-altering drugs.

2 You should not drink any beverages containing caffeine (such as coffee, tea, or cola drinks) for **one hour** before your instruction in meditation. *This abstinence **always** applies but later on need not be more than **half an hour**.*

3 You should not smoke any cigarettes for a **half hour** before your instruction in meditation. *This abstinence applies to your instruction session only. Later on you may smoke moderately before meditation.*

4 You should not eat any food for **one hour** before your instruction in meditation. *This one hour abstinence **always** applies, except in the case of very light meals as described later on in this course.*

5 It is often helpful to loosen all tight clothing and to remove your shoes. If you wear glasses or contact lenses you may want to remove them too. You should feel at ease and physically unhampered while meditating.

Step Six

The room in which instruction is to take place should be arranged so that it contains:

- an audio cassette player close enough to you so that you can conveniently switch it on and off
- a comfortable straight-back chair (if necessary add a pillow to the back) – or, if you prefer to sit on the floor, a cushion placed where you will have some support for your back if needed
- a space in front of the spot where you will be sitting which is entirely free of clutter; all extraneous objects should have been cleared away in this area. Facing a blank wall, or drawn curtains of a subdued colour, or putting up a small screen (or draped material) as a background helps to eliminate distractions

- a place to sit where you can face away from any direct source of light – the room need not be dark, but the lighting should be subdued.

The above arrangements are essential. Meditation occurs when you allow yourself to experience a particular attitude – the 'meditative mood'. When learning meditation, certain arrangements help to establish this mood by setting your instruction session apart from the rest of your life. To help accomplish this, you can make some additional preparations that can contribute to a peaceful, undisturbed atmosphere. While many people find these additional preparations useful (they are set out in Step Seven), if you find them inconvenient or not to your liking, you can omit them and will still learn meditation very satisfactorily if you follow the directions in this course.

Step Seven (Optional additional preparations)

In preparing the room where you will learn meditation, it is useful to arrange the 'scenery' in front of your sitting place in a manner quite different from the way it usually looks. This will be the only time you make such alterations in the room – things will be returned to their former state after you have finished listening to Side 4 of this teaching series. For these optional preparations you will need:

- a low table or stand in front of where you plan to sit
- a potted plant or container with some flowers (or another pleasant object) placed on the table
- if you enjoy the smell of incense, burning it during the learning of meditation can add tranquillity as well as a festive air to the occasion. Avoid overly sweet or artificial scents – ideally you should use a natural scent that gives you a sense of being close to nature. You may also light a candle to help create the special atmosphere. The incense and candle should be lit just before listening to the instruction recording.

Selecting Your Special Sound (Mantra)

The following is a list of sounds/words that have been found to be pleasant and soothing to many people. Read this list over carefully, pronouncing each sound to yourself several times (either mentally or out loud in a soft voice). Then place a mark next to the sound you like best.

(If you prefer to make up your own mantra, see the directions on the following page.)

Note: 'a' is usually pronounced 'ah' in the following words and 'o' is pronounced 'oh', but do whatever pleases you.

ah-nam	tah-sam	shan-ti
shi-rim	ra-ma	sha-lom
see-tah	hush	at-ease
sat-yam	at-man	ma-nah
vis-ta	peace	shee-vo-humm
shahm	hill-lah	gentle

Repeat each of the words above out loud once more. The one that you prefer out of these is your mantra. If you like several equally, then it makes no difference which you choose. Write down your choice in the space below and keep this page of the workbook open in front of you while listening to the instruction recording.

❋ **My mantra choice is: ....**

Important:

1 You do **not** repeat your special sound out loud every time you meditate. This is only necessary when you first learn (during your instruction session). After that, let yourself hear it in your mind.

2 If you want to tell your mantra to a close friend or relative, fine, but do this in a serious manner and request that they keep it confidential. Your mantra should not be discussed lightly because it might lose some of its special effect if it is used when you are not meditating.

The Mantra List

The mantras on the previous page are words from the Sanskrit, Hebrew and English languages which were rated as 'soothing' in a research study at Princeton University. You will notice that many of these words end in the consonants 'm' or 'n', sounds which tend to reverberate in the mind to bring about a state of deep calm. The English words in the list suggest a tranquil state without possessing any harsh or difficult-to-pronounce sounds. The quality of a mantra's sound is the most important factor in the selection of a mantra for relaxation purposes, with its meaning (if known) sometimes serving only to distract. The exception to this rule is when a mantra has been assigned by a meditation teacher for religious or spiritual purposes. Since the aim of CSM is to produce relaxation, translations of any non-English mantras are not given. If you wish to look up the meaning of some of these words that is fine, but I suggest that you first determine the effects of each word's sound on your sense of inner peace, remembering that this is the purpose for which it was chosen.

Creating Your Own Mantra

- Some people find it useful to combine elements of several of the mantras listed on the previous page, to form a new mantra – or you may choose to select a sound not listed here, or make up your own original sound.

- The sound you use should not be agitating. Do not select people's names, or words that have special 'emotionally charged' meanings that may stir you up.
- 'Meaningless' sounds are often effective because they have fewer associations, but it is not essential that a mantra be without meaning. One meditator successfully used the self-created phrase 'peace' as a mantra, and another decided to use the word 'hush' which brought to her mind relaxing images of the sea.
- You may use a religious word or phrase as your mantra, if this would have special meaning for you. Some people choose such a phrase by consulting their religious advisor – others make the choice themselves. The name or phrase chosen should have a positive association for you and be uplifting.

Now look at the list below and the diagram on page 92 to make sure you have not forgotten any essential preparations.

Room Preparations

Dimly lit room
Uncluttered background without distractions
This book open to page where you have written your mantra
Chair or floor cushion
Audio cassette player
Low table or stand (optional)
Plant or other natural object (optional)
Candle (optional)
Incense and matches (optional)

Section 3

LEARNING TO MEDITATE

NOW LISTEN TO INSTRUCTION SESSION – SIDE 3

Post-Instruction Questionnaire

Fill out before listening to the recording (Side 4)

Name	Date	Time
Elaine Shooter	20.6.00	3.42 pm

Complete the following: *Right now after meditating, mentally and physically I feel*

..mentally - calmer, more quiet..........
...physically - muscles more relaxed, but.
...not around head/neck + heart pounding a bit

Mark in the appropriate box **each** of the following words or phrases that accurately describes your first meditation:

1 ❑ Easy
❑ somewhat ❑ extremely ☑ at times ❑ throughout session

2 ☑ Difficult
  ❑ somewhat ❑ extremely ❑ at times ☑ throughout session

3 ❑ Uneven

4 ❑ Carried away

5 ❑ Unsure of myself

6 ❑ Satisfactory

7 ☑ Unsatisfactory

(describe) heart racing

8 ❑ Peaceful

9 ❑ Worried whether I was doing it right

(describe)

10 ☑ Seemed just about the right length

11 ❑ Seemed too long
  ❑ just felt bored ❑ felt extremely restless
  ❑ could barely sit still for another second

12 ❑ Seemed too short
  ❑ felt I definitely needed to continue meditating longer

13 ☑ Felt sleepy during
  ❑ slightly ☑ extremely

14 ❑ Fell asleep
❑ briefly ❑ for most of the session

---

15 ☑ Had many thoughts
❑ pleasant ❑ unpleasant ❑ organized ☑ drifting

---

16 ❑ Had few thoughts
❑ pleasant ❑ unpleasant ❑ organized ❑ drifting

---

17 ❑ Had many visual images
❑ pleasant ❑ unpleasant ❑ of people ❑ of animals
❑ of objects or places ❑ of geometric shapes ❑ of colours

---

18 ❑ Had few visual images
❑ pleasant ❑ unpleasant ❑ of people ❑ of animals
❑ of objects or places ❑ of geometric shapes ❑ of colours

---

19 ☑ Experienced memories
❑ a few ❑ many ❑ ordinary ❑ especially vivid
☑ of recent past ❑ of long ago

---

20 ❑ Experienced moment(s) of total silence
❑ once ❑ several times ❑ for most of session

---

21 ☑ Mantra changed
❑ became louder ☑ softer ❑ speeded up ☑ slowed down
☑ was transformed into different word ❑ became vague pulse
☑ changed rhythm or emphasis

---

22 ❑ Mantra stayed the same throughout

---

23 ❑ Mantra disappeared
❑ momentarily ❑ for several minutes ❑ most of session

---

24 ❑ Mantra linked itself up with breathing
❑ occasionally ☑ about half the time ❑ during whole session

---

25 ☑ There were outer noises
☑ slight ❑ loud

---

26 ❑ Outer noises disturbed me
❑ was able to continue meditating afterwards
❑ was not able to continue meditating afterwards

---

27 ☑ Outer noises didn't bother me

---

28 ❑ Felt physically comfortable throughout session

---

29 ❑ Experienced some physical discomforts during session

(Describe) . . heart racing . . . .

. . . .

---

30 ☑ Felt tense
❑ slightly ❑ extremely ❑ for part of session
☑ for whole session

---

31 ☑ Felt relaxed
☑ slightly ❑ extremely ❑ for part of session
❑ for whole session

Further comments regarding your first meditation:

. . . .

. . . .

. . . .

. . . .

. . . .

If this questionnaire has highlighted any difficulties with your meditation, read the Post-Instruction Advisory Sheet which follows.

Post-Instruction Advisory Sheet

If you marked the following words or phrases in describing your first meditation, follow the recommendations given below for handling any problems encountered. The number corresponding to each question is indicated on the left – *questions not involving problems are not referred to.*

2 It is natural to find a new experience somewhat difficult at times. But if you found your first meditation extremely difficult, and for most of the session, then ask yourself the following:

  a By 'difficult' did you mean that you found yourself struggling against intruding thoughts when meditating? If so, you may not have realised that extraneous thoughts are a natural part of everyone's meditative experience.

  If you have this problem in the future, try greeting these thoughts as you would friends you like but with whom you do not have time to talk right now. Imagine that you are letting these friends walk alongside you, but that you are not becoming involved in conversation with them. In other words, flow *with* the thoughts that turn up during meditation and allow them full play, yet do not cling to them. When the mantra comes to mind again, let the thoughts drift slowly away.

  Sometimes intruding thoughts may be in the foreground of your meditative experience while your mantra continues in the background (almost as though it were 'background music' in a film) ... Sometimes your mantra may be in the foreground with thoughts in the background ... Sometimes you may experience *only* your mantra – no thoughts ... at other times you experience *only* your thoughts – no mantra ... And sometimes you may experience neither, and there may be complete inner stillness. All these different experiences are 'good' and 'right' meditation.

b By 'difficult' did you mean that you had a hard time remembering your mantra, or found it difficult to keep repeating it? If so, you may not have understood how simple and automatic this process can be.

Do not try to 'remember' your mantra or to 'think' it actively. Rather, let the mantra come to you. If this easy attitude results in your hearing your mantra only once or twice during a whole session – that is still meditation. But if you hear it continually during the whole session – that is meditation too. Either way, your sessions can be equally beneficial in terms of their effects on your life.

As you become a practised meditator, the mantra will probably come to you automatically as you sit quietly in meditation, and it may well go away automatically. Simply let it come and go. Don't try to hold on to it. Don't try to repeat it consciously or to force it to establish a rhythm. Don't try to stop it from doing these things. There is no need for any particular rhythm, or pronunciation, or inflection of the mantra. Let yourself find out what the mantra wants to do at any given moment when you allow it to have free rein.

3 If you marked 'uneven', you will find useful discussion about uneven meditation on Side 4. Meditation can be deeply tranquil at times but it can be surface-like and thought-filled at other times. During meditation, activity and rest often follow each other in succession. There will be the 'inward stroke' of each meditation (when everything seems to quiet down), then the 'outward stroke' (when thoughts and restlessness

return) and then the 'inward stroke' again – and so on. Your mind may move back and forth between activity and inactivity as though it were experiencing the peaks and troughs of waves in the sea. When you experience this changing nature of meditation, coast along with it, let yourself be carried on your 'inner sea'.

4 If you marked 'carried away' (and if you felt this to be a problem – not everyone who experiences it finds it so) – you may not realize that such feelings are normal experiences for certain people on certain occasions. If this sense of being 'carried away' feels strange at first, this is probably because you are not used to it. As with a first dive from a high diving board, or when you go skiing for the first time, you may feel uneasy at your first encounter with unusual inner experiences – but with practice you will become more comfortable with them and may find them very meaningful.

Remember, though, that not every meditator experiences moments of being 'carried away' during meditation and your friends may not have such experiences at all, yet their meditations may be every bit as worthwhile as yours.

5 & 9 If you marked 'unsure of yourself' or 'worried whether I was doing it right', you are typical – most of us *are* unsure in new experiences. Remember not to put demands on yourself in meditation. There is no 'right' or 'wrong' in meditation, just as there is no 'right' or 'wrong' in the rhythmic ebb and flow of the tides or in the stirring of wind in the branches of trees. Meditation is a natural process. Watch it without judgement and it will teach you about its own nature.

11 If you marked 'bored', this is not necessarily a problem. You may not feel bored at all during your next

meditation. If you marked that you felt 'extremely restless' or that you 'could barely sit still for another second', then try one or more of the following:

a Keep your eyes partially open during the next meditation session, with your gaze resting on some pleasant natural object.

b Move your limbs or rock slightly during your next meditation session.

c Cut down your meditation time in your next meditation session according to the directions on Side 4.

12 Occasionally a new meditator needs longer sessions of meditation time than are routinely assigned at the beginning of this course. If you experienced an intense need for more time during your first meditation session, try using 20 minutes the next time you meditate. After completing your first 20-minute meditation, observe your reactions. If you had no tension-release side effects (tension-release side effects are described on Sides 4 and 5 of the recordings), or only a few minor effects, then experiment with using 20 minutes as your meditation time from now on. If you experienced a number of uncomfortable tension-release side effects during the 20 minutes, reduce your meditation time to 15 minutes (or back down to 10), the exact reduction depending on the severity of the discomfort. Remain with this reduced time until your meditation stabilises (ie you have no major discomfort), then follow the instructions in your Meditation Adjustment Chart to increase your meditation time again.

13 & 14 If you marked 'felt sleepy' or 'fell asleep', these are *not* problems. Listen to the discussion on Side 4 about handling drowsiness during meditation.

24 If your mantra sometimes linked itself up with your breathing, count yourself among the majority of meditators. Just remember never to *make* your mantra link up with your breathing. In any one session the mantra may be 'in sync' with your breathing or your pulse, or it may not. In this form of meditation, both ways are equally acceptable.

26 If you were unable to continue meditating after being disturbed by some outside noise, try the following the next time you are disturbed in this way:

> On hearing the disruptive sound, stop thinking your mantra and sit quietly with your eyes closed, taking about two minutes to surface slowly. Then come out of meditation and do some quiet (non-strenuous) activity for half an hour. Afterwards, resume meditating and finish off with whatever amount of meditation time is left of your session. Your meditation should be easy and non-stressful now since you are sufficiently removed in time from the irritation of the previous noise. As you become more experienced in meditating, you may very well find that outside noises will be much less disturbing to you and you will be able to get back into meditation immediately after having been interrupted.

29 Momentary physical discomforts (tension-release side effects) are common and you need not be concerned about them unless they are particularly intense or prolonged. If a tension-release side effect lingers after you have finished meditating, try the following:

> Wait for 15 minutes to see if it fades. If it does not, return to meditating, but this time meditate for *less than five minutes*. Do *not* think the mantra now, unless it comes to you automatically (in which case allow it to remain). Instead, place your attention on the discomfort itself, not making any attempt to

make the discomfort disappear, but allowing yourself to feel the discomfort and know it.

Some people describe this process as allowing themselves to 'love the discomfort'. Surprising as it may sound, such an attitude can be extremely effective. If you flow with the discomfort, it is remarkable how often it disappears in the quiet of the meditative state. If it should *not* disappear during meditation, then it is likely to do so within 30 minutes after you stop meditating. In those rare cases where this does not occur, reduce your total meditation time to *no more than five minutes* and stay with this time for one week. After that (if your meditation is proceeding comfortably), build up your meditation time gradually again according to your Meditation Adjustment Chart.

30 If you felt tense at times for part of your session, this was probably a result of releasing tension, which can be a beneficial part of meditation. If you felt *extremely* tense for the *whole session*, reduce your meditation time to five minutes or less, and use this shortened meditation time until your Meditation Adjustment Chart allows you to increase meditation time again.

NOW LISTEN TO POST-INSTRUCTION SESSION – SIDE 4

Your Reaction to CSM

At this point it is useful to ask yourself whether you are the kind of person who:

- needs to keep everything around you neat and orderly
- prefers to have rules spelled out when performing an action (rather than being left on your own)

- needs to be certain while you are performing an activity that you are doing it *correctly*.

If your answer to any (or all) of the above is 'yes', then the method you have just learned from the CSM instruction tape (asking you to allow the meditation to 'go the way it wants to') may not appeal to you as much as a more structured method.

During your instruction session, when practising the technique taught, did you *feel strongly* that you needed more definite rules to follow in order to be able to relax?

If 'yes', turn to page 80 of this workbook – **but only after you have done the following two things:**

1 **Listen to the post-instruction session Side 4**: it contains information which may help you understand your reactions to your first meditation more fully.

2 **Meditate along with the recording 'Timing Your Meditation Practice' on Side 8 of the tapes**. Do so at least once. This recording guides you through your meditation and also offers two very helpful preparatory exercises. These exercises may be all that you need to enable you to become comfortable with your meditation practice. You can then meditate without using the recording or return to it whenever you wish.

Further Instructions for Day 1

Meditating on Your Own

Your instruction calls for you to meditate twice more before playing Side 5 of these recordings. This means that if you learned meditation in the morning or early afternoon, you should meditate once more today and once tomorrow before playing Side 5. If your meditation instruction was in the late afternoon or evening, you should meditate twice tomorrow – once in the morning and once in the afternoon or early evening – before playing Side 5. For these beginning sessions, you should not meditate later than 7 pm. You may be among the 10% of people who become so energized by meditation that they cannot sleep after a late evening meditation. Later on, if you find that you *can* sleep peacefully after meditating late in the evening, then it is fine to meditate after 7 pm.

Adjusting Your Meditation time

Your next two meditation sessions – your first on your own – should be ten minutes (or less) in length, unless you feel that ten minutes was too short and you definitely needed to continue meditating longer *(in which case see 12 on Post-Instruction Advisory Sheet).*

Starting out with a ten-minute meditation time will give you an opportunity to get used to meditating and a chance to estimate what time-span may be best for you at the start.

If ten minutes proves satisfactory in today's and tomorrow's sessions, then (after playing Side 5) you can begin to increase your meditation time gradually, building it up step-by-step towards 20 minutes.

If, on the other hand, you should experience any persistent side effects from meditating for only ten minutes (occasionally this occurs in a new meditator) try the following:

- stay with ten minutes of meditating but keep your eyes open throughout the meditation session *or*
- reduce your meditation time to five minutes per session.

Further instructions for adjusting meditation time are given in the Meditation Adjustment Chart on page 36, which you will use after listening to Side 5.

Day 2 Questionnaire

Fill out after completing the second meditation on your own and just before listening to the recording (Side 5).

Name	Date	Time

Length of meditation sessions, in minutes

Mark in the appropriate box **each** of the following words or phrases that accurately describes your two meditations alone:

1 ❑ Easy
❑ somewhat ❑ extremely ❑ both times ❑ morning only
❑ evening only

2 ❑ Difficult
❑ somewhat ❑ extremely ❑ both times ❑ morning only
❑ evening only

(describe) . . . .

. . . .

3 ❑ Similar to my meditation during the instruction session

4 ❑ Different from my meditation during the instruction session
❑ more satisfactory ❑ less satisfactory ❑ more tranquil
❑ less tranquil

5 ❑ Seemed just about the right length
❑ both times ❑ morning only ❑ evening only

6	❑ Seemed too long, was impatient for session to be over ❑ both times ❑ morning only ❑ evening only
7	❑ Seemed too short, felt frustrated because I needed to meditate longer ❑ both times ❑ morning only ❑ evening only
8	❑ Was at ease with intruding thoughts, accepting them as natural
9	❑ Was concerned about intruding thoughts, struggling to eliminate them
10	❑ Allowed the mantra to come and go, without worrying if it disappeared (if using one of the alternate methods on pages 80–83: I did not worry about losing track of my breathing but simply returned easily to meditation)
11	❑ Was concerned that I was not thinking the mantra enough (if using one of the alternate methods on pages 80–83: I was concerned if I lost track of my breathing or forgot to link it with my mantra)
12	❑ Felt physically and emotionally comfortable throughout the session ❑ both times ❑ morning only ❑ evening only
13	❑ Experienced some physical or emotional discomforts during the session ❑ mild ❑ severe ❑ once or twice ❑ frequently ❑ most or all of the time
14	❑ Was disturbed by intrusive noise ❑ once ❑ several times ❑ repeatedly
15	❑ If interrupted, took plenty of time to 'surface' slowly ❑ on each occasion ❑ some of the time

16 ❑ If interrupted, jumped up to take care of the matter in question
❑ on each occasion ❑ some of the time

---

17 ❑ After interruptions, was able to continue meditating satisfactorily
❑ on each occasion ❑ some of the time

---

18 ❑ After interruptions, was unable to continue meditating satisfactorily
❑ on each occasion ❑ some of the time

---

19 ❑ When starting meditation, spent half a minute or so in restful silence before commencing to think the mantra
❑ both times ❑ morning only ❑ evening only

---

20 ❑ At end of meditation, spent about two minutes in restful silence after stopping the mantra
❑ both times ❑ morning only ❑ evening only

---

21 ❑ Informed others when I was going to meditate
❑ both times ❑ morning only ❑ evening only

---

22 ❑ Silenced my telephone
❑ both times ❑ morning only ❑ evening only

---

23 ❑ Began to notice effects of the meditation on my life outside of meditation
❑ positive ❑ negative

(describe) . . . .

. . . .

---

24 ❑ My mantra spontaneously came to mind outside of meditation
❑ once ❑ a few times ❑ frequently

---

25 ❑ I forgot my mantra during meditation
❑ once ❑ a few times ❑ frequently

---

26 ❑ I had difficulty opening my eyes slowly enough after meditation
❑ in one session ❑ both times

Further comments regarding your two meditations alone:

....

....

....

If this questionnaire has highlighted any difficulties with your meditation, read the Day 2 Advisory Sheet which follows.

Day 2 Advisory Sheet

If you marked the following words or phrases in describing your two meditations alone, follow the recommendations given below for handling any problems encountered. The number corresponding to each question is indicated on the left – *questions not involving problems are not referred to.*

2 If you marked that you found one of your meditation sessions more difficult than the other – were you equally removed from outside pressures (family duties, work, study, etc) when meditating in the morning as compared to the evening? Perhaps outside distractions (sounds, awareness of other people's needs, awareness of some duty of your own) disrupted one of these meditations? If so, observe how your meditation at this hour goes in the future. If it is still unsatisfactory, then consider switching to a quieter time or place where there will be fewer outside distractions or demands. Here are some suggestions:

- **Meditate earlier in the morning**. Some people get up to meditate before the rest of the household and find this an excellent time to meditate undisturbed.

- **Meditate later in the morning**. Some people find that meditating after children have gone to school, or after they have arrived at their place of work, is more satisfactory than meditating before breakfast. If you work in an office during the day, the beginning of your lunch break may also be a good time to meditate – or you may be able to substitute a meditation break for midmorning coffee break.
- **Meditate later in the evening**. Some people find that they can get into the mood of meditation more easily after children have gone to bed or after the chores of the day are completed.
- **Meditate earlier in the evening**. Some people find mid-afternoon (before children come home from school or during an afternoon break at work) to be a quieter time for meditation than late afternoon or evening.

Another way to deal with distractions is to change the location of your meditation sessions. Here are some suggestions:

- **Use a different room**, preferably the least-used room in your home.
- **Meditate somewhere other than your own home:** a library, an unoccupied conference room, a place of worship, an empty room in a neighbour's home are all alternatives that some meditators have reported to be highly satisfactory, but you may discover a still better place.
- **Meditate in a parked car**. Other people will seldom disturb you if they see you seated in a car with eyes closed; they will usually assume that you are napping.
- **Meditate outdoors**. Natural settings are fine to meditate in, weather permitting. Select a peaceful location and meditate at a time of day when there are few insects to disturb you.

- **Meditate while commuting**. Meditating in a bus, plane, train or car is fine. If considering this alternative, read the section of this workbook entitled 'Meditating While Commuting' (page 55).

4 If you marked that you found your first meditations alone to be less satisfactory (or less 'deep') than the meditation you did during your instruction session, this is a common occurrence. When you do meditations on your own they often have to compete with many more distractions than you had during your instruction session and it takes time to get accustomed to this.

In addition, an instruction session is 'special'. While you listened to the instruction recording, you were being guided step by step. In a sense you were being given permission to meditate. When at first you meditate on your own, you may feel a bit uneasy about taking this time for yourself. It may require some time before you get used to allowing yourself the 'luxury' of taking time for yourself out of a busy day.

Also, remember that your meditation need not be a deep or unusual experience to be beneficial. You will appreciate this fact when you begin to see the effects of meditation on your daily life.

6 If you marked that you were impatient for *one* of your meditation sessions to be over (but were not impatient for the *other* to be over), then the timing or location of the troubling session may have been the cause of your difficulty (see 2 above).

If, however, you were impatient for *both* your sessions to be over, reduce your meditation time to seven minutes (or five minutes) per session for the next week (the amount of reduction depending on the degree of your restlessness and discomfort). After one week, consult your Meditation Adjustment Chart and follow the directions for increasing your meditation time again.

7 If you marked that you needed more time during only one of your sessions, add five or ten minutes to that session only. This will result in one of your meditation sessions being longer than the other, which is fine. *(Also see 12 on Post-Instruction Advisory Sheet.)*

9 If you marked that you were struggling to eliminate intruding thoughts during meditation, you may not realize that by fighting *against* them you were strengthening the distracting thoughts. Think what would happen if you were in a crowded street at rush hour (or in any other place where people were packed in close together) and you reacted by shoving the other people out of your way. They would probably start shoving back and an unpleasant situation would develop. In the same way, if you shove intruding thoughts out of the way, they too may begin to 'fight back' – and then you may have difficulty meditating.

It's best to adopt a friendly, accepting attitude towards such thoughts. Realize that the thoughts are there to do their 'job' – to take the stress away from some of your everyday concerns. By allowing these thoughts to go through your mind during meditation it is as if you were running the thoughts through a demagnetizing circuit so that the 'charge' could be taken off of them. Meditators often report that those thoughts that intruded during meditation gradually lost their intensity by the end of the session, so that after meditation they were no longer troubling. Allow intruding thoughts to be there if they appear and let meditation do a 'demagnetizing' job for you. *(Also see 2a on the Post-Instruction Advisory Sheet.)*

11 If you marked that you were concerned that you were not thinking your mantra often enough, you probably do not realize that you are actually meditating, even if you think the mantra only once or twice during an entire meditation session. *(See also 2b on the Post-Instruction*

Advisory Sheet.) Those who are using one of the alternate methods should realize that it is normal to lose the synchronization between breathing and mantra once in a while. Just return easily to linking the two when you realize the count has been lost.

13 If you marked that you experienced some physical or emotional discomforts during meditation, these were probably tension-release side effects. If so, listen to the discussion on side effects on Sides 4 and 5. If the side effects are *severe,* adjust your meditation time accordingly.

14 If you marked that you were disturbed by intrusive noises during your meditation sessions, see 2 in this Advisory Sheet. If noise was your primary concern, you may be particularly sensitive to noise. If so, it can be helpful to realize that many people find outside noises much less disturbing after they have been meditating for a month or more. In the meantime, in addition to shifting the location of your meditation session *(see 2 on this Advisory Sheet)* consider masking the noise by turning on a continuous, monotonous sound. An electric fan or any other low steady sound provides effective screening for most noises.

If you use such a screening device you may become so accustomed to meditating with this monotonous sound in the background that conceivably it could be somewhat difficult for you to meditate without it. To counteract this possibility, schedule a few meditations each week in a quiet location where you can have the experience of meditating *without* using a masking sound. This should adequately preserve the 'portable' quality of your meditation.

16 If you marked that you jumped up *quickly* when interrupted during meditation, realize that the habit of jumping up in response to a demand is instilled in many

of us from early childhood. You may need some 'habit training' to help you develop a leisurely approach to handling interruptions to meditation.

- Arrange for someone to knock on the door while you are sitting with eyes closed in a quiet room. When you hear the knock, start timing yourself, taking 30 seconds to surface slowly. When the 30-second interval is up, walk *deliberately slowly* to the door and open it. *Repeat this exercise ten times in succession.*
- You can, if you wish, use a kitchen timer for this. Simply set the timer at one minute, place it outside your door and then enter the room, sit down and shut your eyes. When the timer rings, follow the steps outlined above.

You may need to do these training exercises daily for as long as a week before slow surfacing becomes second nature to you.

18 If you marked that you were unable to *continue meditating* after being interrupted, you may have surfaced too fast. If so, practise the exercise described in 16 above. If the difficulty still persists, review 26 on the Post-Instruction Advisory Sheet.

24 If you marked that your mantra frequently came to mind outside of meditation, don't worry. No harm will come from spontaneously repeating the mantra in your mind at other times than when meditating. The mantra frequently comes to new meditators during the day because it is something new. Later on it will take its rightful place and probably return only when you 'invite it in'. If you find yourself repeating the mantra during the day, treat the sound as though it were a person whom you are pleased to see, but for whom you have no time at the moment: accept the mantra but do not hold on to it.

25 If you marked that you forgot your mantra during meditation, this is also a common experience for new meditators. If it occurs, try continuing meditating and let yourself become aware of whatever sound comes to you, then use that sound as a mantra. If you decide you like this sound better than your present mantra, you may want to adopt it permanently. If this doesn't work, try stopping meditating, and look up the page in this workbook where you wrote down your mantra.

26 Most people are not accustomed to opening their eyes slowly and some people can never learn to do so. If you find this particularly difficult, try placing both hands over your closed eyes just before it is time to come out of meditation. Your palms should rest against your cheeks with your fingers cupped over your eyes. Be sure to keep your fingers close together so that you shut out light. Now you may open your eyes as quickly as you wish and this will not interrupt your meditation. When you are ready to come out of meditation, start *very slowly* to spread your fingers apart. This creates the same effect as slowly opening your eyes.

This is a good time to begin using your Daily Meditation Checklist on page 89. Start by filling in the squares for the first two meditations done on your own.

NOW LISTEN TO SECOND DAY SESSION – SIDE 5

Handling Problems by Adjusting Meditation Time

Your first two meditations on your own should have been ten minutes or less, unless you felt that ten minutes was definitely too short and that you clearly needed more time, in which case follow directions on page 20 (12). While 20-minute sessions may be satisfactory for some people even at first, they cause some new meditators to release tension too fast for comfort. For this reason, CSM starts most meditators at ten minutes or less, allowing you to increase meditation time gradually as you feel ready.

1 If by any chance you find ten minutes per session *consistently* uncomfortable – either because you are extremely restless or because you experience continuing and unpleasant tension-release side effects – *shorten the time span of your meditation* until you hit on a length that is comfortable for you. You should keep reducing the time until you reach this 'comfort level', even if this eventually results in your meditating for as little as one minute.

2 Once you find your comfort level, stay with it for as many days (or weeks) as you need to, before increasing the length of your meditation sessions again. (When ready to do so consult your Meditation Adjustment Chart.)

3 In the future, if you should find that you are uncomfortable with any particular time-span, cut back to the previous time level and stay with that until you are ready to start increasing your meditation time again.

4 Realize that it is perfectly all right if you decide to remain at any given level on a *permanent* basis. There is no reason why you should be a '15 minute' or '20 minute' meditator, for example, if these are not your preferences.

5 Teenagers have generally reported being most comfortable when they meditate no more than the number of minutes which corresponds to their age: for example, 13 minutes for 13-year-olds. In the future they can, if they wish, increase meditation time by one minute each year.

Meditation Adjustment Chart

In the chart below, the number of days that have elapsed since you learned CSM are shown in the column at the left. Day 1 is your day of learning. Whichever time-span was comfortable for you during your *first two instruction days* is referred to in the column at the right as your 'baseline'. It will almost always be ten minutes or less.

Number of Days Meditating	Time-Span for Meditation
Days 1–4	Remain with Baseline
Days 5–8	Baseline plus 2 minutes
Days 9–12	Baseline plus 4 minutes
Days 13–15	Baseline plus 6 minutes
Days 16–19	Baseline plus 8 minutes
Days 20–22	Baseline plus 10 minutes

After 22 days of meditation, if you are now meditating for 20 minutes, remain with this time-span.[2] It has proven very satisfactory for many people.

If you have not yet reached 20 minutes by the end of 22 days (perhaps because you started with a lower baseline), you may continue to increase your time-span, by two

[2]An occasional meditator finds that after they have been meditating for a while they have a need to meditate longer than 20 minutes. If this is the case with you, you may gradually increase your time-span by adding two minutes at a time, at intervals of three days. Your meditation sessions should not exceed 30 minutes in length during your first year of meditation, however.

minutes at a time, every three days, until you are meditating for 20 minutes. Teenagers represent an exception to this 20-minute rule – see page 36 (5).

Meditation Schedule

(Now is a good time to fill out your meditation schedule.)

Mantra selected: . . . .

Length of meditation session being tried out: . . . minutes

Tentative schedule:

Weekdays:

First meditation:	Time:	am
	Place:	
Second meditation:	Time:	pm
	Place:	

Weekends:

First meditation:	Time:	am
	Place:	
Second meditation:	Time:	pm
	Place:	

Day 9 Questionnaire

Fill out before listening to the recording (Side 6)

Name	Date	Time

Length of meditation sessions, in minutes

Number of times you meditated in the past week

Place a mark in the appropriate box for **each** of the following words or phrases that accurately describes your meditation sessions in the past week:

1 ❑ Easy
❑ somewhat ❑ extremely ❑ occasionally ❑ most of the time

2 ❑ Difficult
❑ somewhat ❑ extremely ❑ occasionally ❑ most of the time

(describe) . . . .

. . . .

3 ❑ Seemed just about the right length

4 ❑ Seemed too long, was impatient for sessions to be over
❑ some sessions ❑ all sessions

5 ❑ Seemed too short, felt frustrated because I needed to meditate longer
❑ some sessions ❑ all sessions

6 ❑ Felt physically and emotionally comfortable throughout sessions
❑ some sessions ❑ all sessions

---

7 ❑ Experienced some physical or emotional discomforts during session
❑ mild ❑ severe ❑ many ❑ few ❑ some sessions ❑ all sessions

(describe) ....

....

---

8 ❑ Noticed effects of meditation on my life *outside* of meditation
❑ positive ❑ negative

(describe) ....

....

---

9 ❑ Was able to establish satisfactory scheduling of meditation routine

---

10 ❑ Was unable to establish satisfactory scheduling of meditation routine

---

11 ❑ Found it easy to sit still during meditation

---

12 ❑ Had trouble keeping still during meditation

---

13 ❑ Found it easy to keep my eyes closed during meditation

---

14 ❑ Kept wanting to open my eyes during meditation

---

15 ❑ Used the Meditation Adjustment Chart for regulating my meditation

---

16 ❑ Have been using the Meditation Checklist to record my meditation

---

17 ❑ Found it easier to schedule-in meditations on weekend

---

18 ❑ Found it more difficult to schedule-in meditations on weekend

---

19 ❑ When starting meditation, spent half a minute or so in restful silence before commencing to think mantra
❑ always ❑ sometimes

---

20 ❑ At end of meditation, spent about two minutes in restful silence after stopping the mantra
❑ always ❑ sometimes

---

21 ❑ Silenced my telephone
❑ always ❑ sometimes

---

22 ❑ Was bothered because I could not tell whether or not I was meditating correctly
❑ slightly bothered ❑ extremely bothered

Further comments regarding first week's meditation:

. . . .

. . . .

. . . .

. . . .

. . . .

. . . .

. . . .

If this questionnaire has highlighted any difficulties with your meditation, read the Day 9 Advisory Sheet which follows.

Day 9 Advisory Sheet

If you marked the following words or phrases in describing your first meditation, follow the recommendations given below for handling any problems encountered. The number corresponding to each question is indicated on the left – *questions not involving problems are not referred to.*

2 If you marked that you had *extreme* difficulties *occasionally*, reduce your meditation time to five minutes per session, stay with this time for one week and then increase your meditation time gradually according to the Meditation Adjustment Chart.

If you marked that you had *extreme* difficulty *most* of the time, stop meditating entirely for five days, after which commence meditating again, but for only three to five minutes per session. If this length proves satisfactory, then begin to increase your meditation time gradually according to your Meditation Adjustment Chart.

If your meditation is still extremely difficult after using the above strategies, try eyes-open meditation or moving meditation *(listen again to descriptions of these on Side 5).* If neither of these variations help, then stop meditating entirely. Later on you may want to seek special instruction from a meditation teacher, or perhaps use some other form of meditation, but for now you would do best to give yourself at least a month's rest from the practice.

4 & 5 If you marked that your meditation does not feel as though it were a suitable length, study your Meditation Adjustment Chart and experiment during this next week with different meditation times until you find the one that is comfortable for you. You might also try some variations on the meditation technique (keeping eyes open, or moving slightly as described on Side 5).

7 If you are continuing to experience severe physical or emotional discomfort during sessions, review the guidance in 13 on the Day 2 Advisory Sheet.

10 If you are still having difficulty establishing a satisfactory schedule for your meditation, review the suggestions in 2 on the Day 2 Advisory Sheet.

Also, realize that doing a shorter meditation on occasions when you can't fit in a regular-length meditation is better than omitting meditation entirely. You may decide to plan full meditations twice daily *when you can*, but settle for a short meditation rather than none at all on those occasions when a full meditation is difficult.

12 See discussion in 4 and 5 above.

14 If you marked that you had difficulty keeping your eyes closed, allow your eyes to remain partially open. Gaze quietly at some pleasant object (such as a green plant) without staring at it. Shift your gaze whenever you need to.

18 Weekends present special problems for some people. Read 2 on the Day 2 Advisory Sheet for suggestions on how to handle this. Also see discussion in numbers 4 and 5 above with respect to using shorter meditations at times when you cannot fit in a longer one.

22 If you marked that you are *extremely* bothered because you cannot tell whether you are meditating correctly – and if my advice about there being no 'right' or 'wrong' way to meditate has not helped you – then try meditating in a manner that enables you to check on whether you are doing it correctly by learning one of the alternate methods of meditating on pages 80–83. If you are already using one of the alternate methods but are still worried about whether you are meditating 'correctly', realize that as long as you are linking up the

mantra with your breathing in the prescribed manner at least *part of the time*, this is correct meditation.

NOW LISTEN TO NINTH DAY SESSION – SIDE 6

Section 4

HELPING MEDITATION WORK

The following is a review of points made in the recordings plus some further hints. Reading this section will help to 'set' these points in your memory.

Basic Facts

- Plan to meditate regularly twice daily during your 'adjustment period' (the first three weeks). To be effective, meditation needs to become a regular routine in your life.
- Ordinarily you will not meditate on a full stomach. It is all right if once in a while you meditate after a very light meal, if this is necessary because of your schedule, but after a full meal always wait at least one hour.
- The caffeine contained in coffee, tea or cola drinks is a stimulant and may counteract the calming effects of meditation. These drinks should be avoided for the hour before meditating.

Times of Day for Meditation

- An ideal time for your first meditation is in the morning before breakfast. First, get out of bed and sit in a chair (or on the floor if you prefer). It may be useful to walk around a bit and to wash so as to be thoroughly awake before starting to meditate, but avoid strenuous physical exercise, unless you can give yourself about 20 minutes to quiet down fully, following the exercise. However, the use of 'meditative' exercises beforehand – such as Yoga stretches, breathing exercises, or T'ai Chi – may help your meditation. If you are unable to meditate before breakfast, you can meditate effectively after finishing a very light breakfast (without caffeine), or at midmorning, or just before lunch. It is useful to space your two meditations so they are at least three to four hours apart. Occasionally, your schedule may mean doing your first meditation in the afternoon. This can be a satisfactory arrangement, providing that you allow enough time to elapse before your next meditation session.
- An ideal time for your second meditation of the day is in the late afternoon, before dinner. This gives you a break which seems to 'wash away' the accumulated tensions of the day, giving you a 'second wind' for the evening hours. If before-dinner meditation is not convenient, wait at least an hour after eating before meditating.
- People who have particularly long and busy days may wish to try meditating at bedtime. Most people find that this is relaxing and easily fall asleep afterwards. Some people, however, report that late evening meditation makes them so energetic that they stay up until all hours of the night. You may want to find out for yourself whether you are among the large majority of people for whom bedtime meditation is sleep-inducing, or one of

the minority who is so energized by it they have difficulty falling asleep afterwards.

Handling Interruptions

Your meditation should be practised in a reasonably quiet place where you are not too likely to be disturbed. Your telephone should be silenced.[3] Non-meditating adults, children or animals should be out of the room while you are meditating.

If, despite all precautions, you *are* interrupted during your meditation session – *play for time*. Take 20 to 30 seconds to come out of meditation slowly before dealing with the interruption. This will give you ample time to 'surface'. After disposing of the matter in question, return to your meditation and finish off with the time that is left. A useful strategy for avoiding interruption is to place a 'signal' on the outside of your door to indicate to others that you are meditating; they often do not realize this unless informed.

Drowsiness During Meditation

Falling asleep during meditation sometimes occurs. When it does, it is a signal that you need sleep more than meditation at that particular moment. Never fight sleep. If it comes, let it. If you are in a place where it is convenient to lie down and take a nap, by all means do so (it is apt to be a particularly restful nap under these circumstances), and when you awaken, finish off with five minutes of meditation.

[3]Do this by switching off the ringer or unplugging the telephone. If you can do neither on your telephone, dial your own number and leave the handset off the hook. This will create a busy signal for incoming callers.

Timing Your Meditation

Most people find the use of a timer disturbing. Sometimes you may need to take a minute or two longer in a particular session: the timer will not 'know' this, but you will. It is best to time meditation by occasionally peeking at a watch or a clock placed conveniently in front of you so you do not need to turn your head to see it. You should do this by squinting with one eye only: this is less apt to rouse you from meditation than opening both eyes wide. After they are experienced at meditating, many people learn to sense when their meditation time is up, as though they had a built-in timer. If you do find it more convenient to use a timer, make sure the alarm sound is not jarring. Placing the timer under cushions can work well.

> The recording on Side 8, Timing and Renewing Your Meditation Practice, is for optional use with your regular meditations. It carries two preparatory exercises to help deepen your practice and provides timing for 10, 15 and 20 minute meditations.

Starting Your Session

Although you did not do this during your instruction session, when meditating on your own it is useful to begin each session by sitting quietly for about half a minute before commencing the mantra. This gives your body and mind a chance to settle down and prepare for meditation. *Meditation should begin and end in quiet and restful silence.*

Ending Your Session

Always take two to three minutes to come out slowly after finishing meditating. Remain sitting quietly during this time with your eyes closed – without thinking your mantra. This quiet interval will help you to carry over the relaxing effects of meditation into your daily life. *Remember that meditation should begin and end in quiet and restful silence.*

Posture During Meditation

There is no 'right' position for CSM so you can experiment and discover what posture is most comfortable for you. Ordinarily it is not a good idea to lie down to meditate (except under special circumstances such as illness or extreme fatigue) because the lying-down position is closely associated with sleep. If you lie down when meditating you may automatically bring on sleep. Your mantra may, in this way, become a sleep-inducing stimulus rather than one that brings about a state of alert restfulness. As pointed out, it is all right if you *happen* to fall asleep during meditation, but it is not a good idea to intentionally fall asleep in this way. Nevertheless, some people find that lying down is the most acceptable way for them to meditate. Your individual reaction should determine your final decision.

Some meditators experience neck strain during meditation because they have allowed their head to drop too far forward, exerting a pull on the neck muscles. If your head drops this way when meditating and if this becomes a problem, consider sitting with your head propped back against a high-back chair or a wall.

Using the Mantra

Despite instructions to the contrary, occasionally meditators feel compelled to 'grab' at their mantra. They force themselves to keep thinking about it. Once again I repeat my original suggestion – that you think your mantra repeatedly *as long as it comes to mind* – but otherwise let your thoughts, feelings, fantasies and visual images go where they will. CSM offers you a rest from 'forcing'. (If you are using one of the alternate methods of meditation you should allow the mantra to link with each breath in a natural, easy manner without any forcing.)

Special Situations

- If you should find that you *consistently* have difficulty sitting still during meditation, it may be helpful to allow yourself to move in a rhythmical way while meditating – rocking gently, nodding your head, opening and closing your hands, or making other small repetitive movements.
- If you find it especially difficult to keep your eyes shut, try repeating the mantra with eyes open, gazing quietly at some pleasant natural object.
- You may find that your mantra naturally links itself up with your breathing at times. This is fine. Simply remember not to force your mantra to stay in rhythm with your breathing. Let the meditation proceed in its own way without influence *(unless you have selected one of the alternative breathing meditation methods on pages 80–83 in which case it is proper to link the mantra to every breath).*
- It may not be wise to use CSM as a means of putting yourself to sleep at night, although some people have reported the successful use of mini-meditations (described on page 75 and Side 6) for this purpose. If you wish to, you can use another form of meditation to induce sleep. Counting each out-breath up to '10', and then repeating this sequence will not interfere with your regular meditation. *(Or you can try one of the alternative methods described on pages 80–83 for this purpose.)*
- Extra meditations (more than two per day) *are* permitted under special circumstances, as follows:

  1 When you are suffering from a temporary illness or

preceding or following surgery, you may do as many meditations a day as you feel you need until your condition returns to normal.

2 When you are suffering from an emotional shock brought about by persons or events in the outside world, extra meditations can be helpful. Circumstances which warrant this are natural disasters (floods, fires, earthquakes, etc) and personal traumas (assaults, bereavements, accidents, etc). You may meditate as often as you need under these circumstances, but make sure that you return to your regular twice (or once) daily meditation routine once conditions have returned to normal.

3 When you are suffering from an unusual amount of tension you may add an extra meditation to your daily routine for as long as the unusual stress continues – returning to twice or once a day meditation as soon as the condition returns to normal.

Strategies for Reducing Tension with Meditation

- A particularly effective way to use extra meditations when under stress is to take your regular meditation session and then one hour later follow it by another full meditation session. Scheduled this close on the heels of your usual session, the additional meditation seems to take up where the regular meditation left off and may greatly intensify the relaxing effects of meditation.
- Those who have been meditating for more than one year may elect to reduce persistent tension in a different manner – by *staying with their meditation* until they feel the tension melting away. Doing this may mean meditating for as long as 45 minutes in a single session. This strategy is to be used only when exceptional

amounts of tension are present, that way it will not become a habit and will not result in over-meditation. Some meditators report that at a certain moment during such a prolonged session, the tension dissipates suddenly, within a matter of a few seconds, and that the feeling is as though a 'road block' had been removed. Other meditators report that the tension begins to fade gradually after they remain in meditation for this longer period of time.

Sensible Precautions

- It is not wise to meditate when taking a bath in case you fall asleep.
- If you plan to meditate after taking medicine prescribed by your doctor, use good judgement. Sleeping medication sometimes makes people too 'groggy' to meditate and diet pills may make them too restless. Most prescribed medications, however, do not affect meditation.
- Do not meditate while driving a car or operating machinery since meditation sometimes causes drowsiness.
- Do not meditate with anything in your mouth (such as chewing gum) because you may swallow it inadvertently while in this relaxed state.
- Do not meditate while under the influence of alcohol or any mind-altering drugs. Meditation requires clear-headedness.

Special Problems and Exceptional Circumstances

High degree of tension-release: If you are experiencing an exceptional amount of tension-release when first learning meditation, and if none of the strategies suggested in this workbook (or on the recordings) have relieved it – *then stop meditating entirely for five days*. After that you can gradually recommence your practice – meditating only *once* a day instead of twice – for five minutes or less at a time. If this new routine proves satisfactory, stay with it for two weeks and then experiment by building up your meditation time little by little according to your Adjustment Chart, but wait until you feel thoroughly comfortable before going back to meditating twice a day. Some people even prefer to adopt once-a-day meditation on a permanent basis.

'Out of body' experiences: A minute percentage of meditators have reported that during meditation they have felt as though they were detached from their bodies, floating in space where they 'could look back at their own selves'. If you should have such an experience, it needs to be controlled just like any other excessive reaction. A person experiencing an 'out of body' episode can usually control it satisfactorily by suggesting to themselves beforehand that they can easily and comfortably 'return to their body' at will. The following strategies have proved useful in this respect:

a Opening your eyes while meditating usually stops the 'out of body' experience automatically by orienting you to your surroundings.

b During future meditations, you should repeat the following verbal suggestion out loud at the commencement of each meditation session, just before closing your eyes: 'When I am meditating I am in complete control of myself and can return to my body any time I wish.'

c Meditators who have had an 'out of body' experience should cut down sharply on the time they spend in meditation to prevent themselves from going too deeply into meditation. This reduced meditation time should then be adhered to until they find that they can enter the meditative state without *uncontrolled* 'out of body' experiences. (Reduction of meditation time may control these experiences without the necessity of applying any of the previous measures suggested.)

Panic attacks: A very small percentage of meditators who are suffering from emotional problems have reported that they experienced an episode of extreme panic when meditating. Such episodes can be handled as follows:

a Open the eyes immediately and use the following breathing techniques:
Allow yourself to breathe slowly, deeply, fully, imagining that each breath is going down into your stomach, so that you are breathing with the stomach, rather than with the chest. Slow, easy breathing using abdominal muscles is very calming, particularly if you follow the progress of the inward and outward flow of breath in the lungs by moving one finger up and down before your eyes in a steady, unbroken pace; this should be done without stopping at either the end of the in-breath (the peak of the wave) or at the end of the out-breath (the trough of the wave). Instead, your finger should trace continuous waves in the air and the breathing should follow these imaginary continuous waves. This way the breath will gradually become steady and even. Slow, even breathing is the opposite of the irregular breath pattern accompanying panic. By slowing down your breathing and allowing it to become deep and even, you will usually regain a sense of calm and centredness.

b Also, should you experience a panic attack you should cut down sharply on your meditation time, or perhaps even stop meditating altogether for a week or so and then resume the practice as shown in the Meditation

Adjustment Chart. If the attack is severe, meditation should be resumed only in consultation with a psychotherapist or counsellor.

A Realistic Compromise

Keep in mind the fact that doing a shorter meditation on occasions when you cannot fit in a regular length meditation is much better than omitting meditation entirely. If you follow an extremely tight schedule, you may decide to plan full meditations twice daily *when you can*, but settle for a short meditation rather than none at all on those occasions when a full meditation is difficult.

Trial Period

If you stop meditating before you have been practising meditation for *at least four months*, you will not have given meditation a full trial. A number of people first notice benefits from meditation only after they have been meditating more than three and a half months and a very small percentage first notice benefits only after meditating more than four months. For example, many meditators report that they consume less alcohol than before, but this result is often not evident until they have been meditating for three to six months. Reductions in cigarette smoking may take even longer to appear – the most substantial reductions usually being seen after the person has been meditating more than one or two years.

Therefore, if you are not having any persistent and undesirable side effects (as described in this course) I suggest that you continue meditating regularly for at least four months. Even though you might be seeing no benefits from your practice as yet, you may be surprised at the benefits you will notice as time goes on.

If You Find Meditation Incompatible

A few individuals practising well-known forms of meditation have had sufficiently unsatisfactory experiences with meditation in the first few weeks that their inner wisdom has prompted them to abandon the practice. In the absence of a personal meditation teacher, my recommendation is that if, for any reason, you find the technique of meditation described here in any way distressing or unpleasant *and* if you have not been able to remedy this situation by using any of the suggested variations in routine, then you should quietly give yourself permission to set meditation aside. Perhaps at some future time you may feel that it is desirable to give it another try – perhaps not. Each person should respect their own intuitions as to whether this practice is suitable for them. If by any chance you do not find meditation compatible, simply stop practising it.

Meditating While Commuting

Many people find meditating while travelling to and from work an excellent solution to the problem of finding time to meditate. It ensures regular scheduling of meditation, helping to establish it as a permanent habit. If you plan to do this, keep in mind the following:

People vary in their initial response to meditating in a public vehicle. Some can meditate when commuting as soon as they have learned meditation; the plan works well from the beginning. Others find meditating while commuting to be unsatisfactory at first, but are still able to do it, and later it becomes easy with practice. Still others find it necessary to get used to meditating in a quiet place and then (usually after the three-week adjustment period is over) find themselves able to meditate comfortably in a public vehicle. Determine in which of these three categories you belong, plan accordingly, and note the following:

1 You can meditate on buses, trains, planes, or in cars (when someone else is driving). *Do not* meditate while *driving* a car or any other vehicle.

2 Although there is nothing wrong with having people in a public place know that you are meditating, those around you will probably think you are napping.

3 When commuting, you may hear a background buzz of conversation and may even be able to make out words of a nearby conversation. Most commuters find this is not detrimental to meditation, providing no one is talking directly *to* them or demanding a response *from* them. Impersonal sounds can easily be tuned-out or incorporated into the rhythms of the meditation in a way that renders them undisturbing, and some meditators even report that the buzz of conversation and the sounds of the moving vehicle contribute to the peacefulness of their meditations.

4 It is useful to decide which part of your trip is best for meditating; some parts have fewer stops and less distractions.

Learning Meditation When Bedridden

People who are confined to bed because of illness or who are preparing for surgery can learn meditation very satisfactorily. Note the following:

1 You should not learn meditation when running a fever. Raised temperatures make the mind race, which can block meditation.

2 Obtain the cooperation of your friends, family, or if in the hospital, of the hospital staff. Make certain that no one interrupts you for a *full hour* during your instruction session.

3 If you are confined to bed, you may need help with

positioning a tape recorder near enough to you so that you can turn over the recordings, or may need to arrange for someone to do this for you. In order not to make you self-conscious (if you decide on the latter), your assistant should either meditate along with you while you learn, or else face away from you.

4 If possible, arrange to be propped up by a pillow or have your bed slightly raised while learning meditation. This helps maintain wakefulness during the session, but if this is not possible, meditation can be learned in the lying down position.

5 If your physical condition prevents you from pronouncing the mantra out loud during the instruction, simply think the mantra to yourself when told to 'say it' by your instructor. You may want to move a finger or your eyelids or some other part of your body slightly at the same time in rhythm with your mantra. Allow these movements to become less and less energetic as the instructions indicate to repeat the mantra 'more and more softly'. These motions should cease altogether with the instructions on the recording to 'think the mantra silently without moving lips or tongue'.

6 If you have an acute illness with high amounts of physical stress, you may do more than the ordinary number of meditations a day, even from the beginning. If, however, you are bedridden because of a long-standing chronic illness, start out with exactly the same schedule of meditation time prescribed in this course for non-bedridden people.

7 Obtain the cooperation of your doctor in your meditation programme. He or she needs to know you are meditating because meditation sometimes results in a decreased need for certain drugs such as tranquillizers, painkillers, or sedatives. It may even

decrease the need for insulin or anti-hypertensive medication. If you are in hospital, your doctor can also be of help in seeing to it that the hospital staff respect your need to meditate without interruption.

8 Meditation can be learned by people who are taking most prescribed medications. Exceptions to this are drugs that alter the state of alertness of the individual such as the major painkillers or sleeping pills. If you have been prescribed a drug that radically changes your consciousness, either wait until such time as your doctor no longer feels it necessary to prescribe this drug, or else plan to learn meditation after a dose of the drug has worn off and before the next dose is administered. In the light of recent evidence that meditation can be useful in reducing pain, the learning of meditation should be encouraged if the handling of pain is a problem.

Combining Exercise and Meditation

While it is important to wait 15 minutes after strenuous exercise before doing your regular sitting meditation, once you are accustomed to meditating (ie after the three-week adjustment period is up) it is possible to combine meditation effectively with repetitive forms of exercise such as jogging, swimming, walking and cycling.

Do this by mentally repeating your mantra in rhythm with the exercise you are performing (if you are walking you may want to repeat the mantra to yourself with every step, or with every other step). Meditating while exercising can result in increased physical efficiency and also lessen the monotony of certain types of exercise such as running indoors. Athletes who combine repetitive exercise with meditation frequently report less fatigue and more ease of body movements.

Meditating while exercising does *not* constitute part of your regular meditation routine for the day. It can therefore be done in addition to your two regular meditations. For people who are extremely active and find it exceedingly difficult to sit still for regular meditation sessions, meditating while exercising can be substituted for the regular sessions.

Three Months' Evaluation

1 *Checking Your Meditation Routines and Attitudes*

This is a quiz with a scoring key that shows you where you stand with regard to your current meditation practice and (if necessary) the steps that can be taken to improve it. It is highly recommended that you take this quiz as soon as you have completed three months of meditating.

2 *Three Months' Follow-up Questionnaire*

This consists of a series of questions aimed at focusing attention on your own meditative experience.

Unlike the other questionnaires in this workbook there is no advisory sheet that goes with this one. Filling out the Three Months' Follow-up Questionnaire helps you realize certain things that have been going on that may have escaped your attention. I recommend it to those who are interested in exploring their meditative experience more fully.

Checking Your Meditation Routines and Attitudes

Place a mark in the appropriate box for *each* of the following words or phrases that accurately describes your meditative practice at present. When answering a question that does not apply to your experience, answer as you *think* you would behave.

- ❑ If I experience difficulties in meditation, I consult the workbook for suggestions on how to handle them.
- ❑ Meditation is now established as a regular habit in my life.
- ❑ I have found a reasonably satisfactory place (or places) for my meditation.
- ❑ I have been able to find satisfactory times of day for meditating.
- ❑ I feel comfortable adjusting my own meditation time upwards or downwards according to my needs.
- ❑ I can allow the mantra to come and go, without worrying if it disappears. (If I use one of the alternate methods, I do not worry if I lose track of my breathing but just return my attention to it easily.)
- ❑ I can allow the mantra to change any way it 'wishes'.
- ❑ I seldom (or never) force myself to think the mantra, but allow the thought of it to enter my mind just as it 'wants to'. (If I use one of the alternate methods, I link the mantra with each breath without forcing and do not blame myself when I occasionally lose track.)
- ❑ I experience my meditation as a personal experience, realizing it may be quite different from the meditation of others.
- ❑ I feel comfortable with the 'ups' and 'downs' (changing qualities) of my different meditation sessions.
- ❑ I begin and end each meditation session by sitting in restful silence.
- ❑ When interrupted during meditation, I automatically surface slowly and get up in a leisurely manner.
- ❑ I regularly return to finish my meditation after interruptions.

- ❑ I don't ask anything of my meditation but watch what it brings.
- ❑ I record each completed meditation on my daily Meditation Checklist.
- ❑ I do not judge the success of my meditation by how I feel during any particular session, but take a long-range view.
- ❑ If I should skip a meditation session or take a break from meditation, I don't feel that I have stopped meditating.
- ❑ I don't worry about whether I am doing meditation 'right' or 'wrong'.
- ❑ If sleepiness comes during meditation, I am not concerned if I fall asleep, and allow myself a nap.
- ❑ I trust my own inner wisdom with respect to what is best for me in my meditation.

To Score: Credit yourself with five points for each statement that you marked in the above list. Total your points and enter score below.

Date of Quiz	Score	Date of Quiz	Score

Additional spaces above are for use in retaking this quiz at intervals. I suggest you retake it every three to four months. Obtaining an up-to-date meditation score helps you keep a check on your practice, recognize and enjoy your own progress, and be alert to any emerging problems.

Scoring for Quiz on Meditation Routines and Attitudes

Score of 86–100 You have established an excellent routine of meditating. You see your meditation as your own experience and can freely adjust it to suit your own needs. This suggests that you are well on your way to a long-term practice of meditation with fine results.

Score of 71–85 You are doing extremely well. There are, however, a few areas which, if given attention at this point, will help you establish an even more satisfactory practice of meditation. Note the questions that you did *not* mark as 'yes' on the quiz and consult the index at the end of this workbook to locate advice concerning these aspects of your meditation practice.

Score of 51–70 You are meditating satisfactorily on many levels, but still have some unsolved problems that need to be worked on. Note the questions that you did *not* mark as 'yes' on the quiz and consult the index at the end of this workbook to locate advice concerning these aspects of your meditation practice. In addition, play your Instruction Session Recording (Side 3) again. Such a review of the teaching often brings new life into the meditation practice.

Score of 31–50 You are facing some troublesome difficulties with your meditation routine. It is important that you note the questions that you did *not* mark as 'yes' on the quiz and consult the index at the end of this workbook to locate advice concerning these aspects of your meditation practice. You should also make plans to go through your meditation training programme again from start to finish, including your introductory and instructions sessions. This second time through should help clear up the problems you are facing.

Score of 0–30 Your meditation is in serious difficulty and you may be in danger of dropping out of meditation without having had the opportunity to find out if it can be valuable for you. If you wish to remedy this situation, it is essential that you retake this entire course *as soon as possible* – starting from the beginning (the introductory talks) and listening to all the recordings, one by one. You may choose a different mantra this time if you wish – a change at this point is sometimes refreshing – or if you have been using the main technique taught in this course, you might find it useful to switch to one of the alternative methods described on pages 80–83.

This time through the course be sure to follow *every step* as you go along, even if you didn't the first time. Fill out each questionnaire and consult the corresponding advisory sheet. If you filled out the questionnaires before, use a different coloured pen or pencil this time so as not to confuse your present answers with your former ones. Retaking the course should be of great help, allowing you to grasp points you may have misunderstood or skimmed over the first time.

Three Months' Follow-Up Questionnaire

Name . . . . Date . . . .

1 During the past three months, how often have you been meditating on average? Circle the appropriate letter. If you wish, you may comment in the space provided.

a Regularly twice a day . . . .

b Sometimes twice a day, sometimes once . . . .

c Once a day . . . .

d Several times a week . . . .

e Once weekly . . . .

f Only occasionally . . . .

g Not at all . . . .

2 Did you stop meditating for any prolonged period of time?
❑ Yes ❑ No. If 'yes', give approximate length of time you were *not* meditating:

. . . .

3 Some people have reported the following reactions to the experience of meditating. Describe your own reactions by circling all letters that apply. (If you wish, you may comment in the space provided):

a Interesting . . . .

b Boring . . . .

c Irritating . . . .

d Useful . . . .

e Relaxing . . . .

f An imposition . . . .

g Anxiety provoking . . . .

h Enjoyable . . . .

i Other (*describe*) . . . .

. . . .

4 The following is a list of personality traits and emotional tendencies which are sometimes reported as having changed in some manner with meditation. Describe your own experience since commencing meditation (circle the appropriate letters).

	Increased	**No Effect**	**Decreased**
Hostility	a	b	c
Energy level	a	b	c
Tension	a	b	c
Enthusiasm	a	b	c
Efficiency	a	b	c
Ability to concentrate	a	b	c
Tendency to be depressed	a	b	c
Productivity	a	b	c
Ability to relate to others	a	b	c
Dependency on others	a	b	c
Decisiveness	a	b	c
Awareness of external environment	a	b	c
Awareness of inner feelings	a	b	c
Boredom	a	b	c
Awareness of own opinions	a	b	c
Happiness	a	b	c
Rigidity	a	b	c
Clarity of thought	a	b	c
Spontaneity	a	b	c
Vividness of perceived colours	a	b	c
Self-assertion	a	b	c
Irritability	a	b	c
Clarity of perceived sounds	a	b	c
Sense of separate identity	a	b	c

	Increased	No Effect	Decreased
Creativity	a	b	c
Emotional aliveness	a	b	c
Insecurity	a	b	c
Tranquillity	a	b	c
Restlessness	a	b	c
Pessimism	a	b	c
Ability to be angry when called for	a	b	c
Finding time for myself during the day	a	b	c
Critical of myself	a	b	c
Influenced by the opinion of others	a	b	c
Feeling important to myself	a	b	c
Intolerant of own mistakes or awkwardness	a	b	c
Taking minor inconveniences lightly	a	b	c
Effective planning of time	a	b	c
Ability to say 'No'	a	b	c

If there are changes you have observed, for the better or for the worse, which are not listed above, describe these:

. . . .

. . . .

. . . .

. . . .

5 Have persons close to you noticed any changes in you? If so, describe:

. . . .

. . . .

. . . .

. . . .

6 Do you feel that meditation has had any effect on your attitude towards work or school? (Circle the appropriate letters.)

	Improved	**Worsened**	**No Effect**	**Not Applicable**
Work	a	b	c	d
School	a	b	c	d

7 Do you feel that meditation has affected your health?
❑ Yes ❑ No. (If so, how?)

. . . .

. . . .

. . . .

. . . .

8 Have you ever used meditation during a diagnosed illness? If so, how often? Was it helpful?

. . . .

. . . .

. . . .

. . . .

. . . .

9 Have you ever done extra meditations (or simply repeated your mantra to yourself) to cope with a specific anxiety situation (eg at the dentist)? If so, describe:

. . . .

. . . .

. . . .

. . . .

. . . .

10 Have you ever experimented with variations in your meditation routine (another mantra; different lengths of time; increased/ decreased frequency; musical or other sound accompaniments; eyes

open; moving while you meditate; breathing exercises, etc)? If so, describe:

. . . .

. . . .

. . . .

. . . .

. . . .

11 Do you vary posture? If so, how?

. . . .

. . . .

. . . .

12 In your opinion, do you feel that meditation has affected your relationship with any of the following groups? Circle one letter in each row:

	Improved	**Worsened**	**No Effect**	**Not Applicable**
Parent(s)	a	b	c	d
Sister(s)/Brother(s)	a	b	c	d
Boyfriend/Girlfriend/ Spouse/Partner	a	b	c	d
Children	a	b	c	d
Close friend(s)	a	b	c	d
Co-worker(s)	a	b	c	d
Employer/Boss	a	b	c	d
Others	a	b	c	d

Comments . . . .

. . . .

. . . .

. . . .

Indicate the effect of meditation on the following habits, by circling the letter next to the statements which best describe your experience. If a

given statement does not apply to you, write 'N/A' (not applicable) in the margin before the number.

13 If, before you began meditating, you used to have some trouble sleeping, is your sleep now:

   a more troubled than formerly

   b usually sound

   c the same

14 If, before you began meditating, your sleep was usually sound, do you have:

   a some trouble sleeping

   b no change

   c even sounder sleep

15 If, before you began meditating, you used to wake up feeling tired, do you now:

   a wake up feeling rested

   b see no change

   c wake up feeling more tired

16 If, before you began meditating, you used to wake up feeling rested, do you now:

   a wake up feeling tired

   b see no change

   c wake up feeling more rested

17 If, before you began meditating, you used to sleep too long, do you now:

   a see no change

   b not sleep quite so long

18 In comparison to before you began meditating, do you now require:

   a more sleep

   b less sleep

   c same amount of sleep

19 In comparison to before you began meditating, do you now handle stressful situations:

a more easily

b less easily

c same as before

20 In comparison to before you began meditating; following a stressful incident, do you now recover:

a at same rate as before

b less rapidly

c more rapidly

21 Have you noticed any change in your value system or outlook on life since commencing meditation? If so, describe:

. . . .

. . . .

. . . .

. . . .

Enhancing Your Meditation

As you become accustomed to meditating you may find that your sense of well-being has been increased and that you now want to go further. Here are some suggestions:

1 Before commencing your meditation session, do one or two minutes of Progressive Muscle Relaxation. This is done by alternately tensing and relaxing your major muscle groups. Start with your toes and proceed upward, tensing and relaxing in turn the muscles in your calves; thighs, buttocks, lower abdomen, arms, hands, shoulders, neck (to tense neck, press it back against a pillow), jaw, mouth, eyes and forehead. If you wish to shorten this procedure, tense and relax only those parts of your body which are your own particular

tension areas (such as upper back, neck, etc).

With each muscle group, tighten the muscles involved just enough so that you *feel* them. Do not overdo the tensing part (this is not a form of physical exercise). When you recognize the feeling of tension, then 'let go' and allow the tension to drain away from this area. Follow by allowing it to drain still more … and more …

There is no need to *work* at relaxing – relaxation is an absence of work. All you need do to release muscle tension is 'a whole lot of nothing'. This quiet relaxing of your body, starting with your toes and proceeding up to your forehead, can greatly contribute to the peacefulness of the meditation session that follows.

2 Before commencing your meditation session, do one or two minutes of deep abdominal breathing as described on page 53. This can deepen the meditative mood.

3 Before commencing your meditation session, spend five minutes listening to music which is 'meditative'; perhaps the slow movement of a Baroque composition or any other music that will be effective for you.

Note: Do not play the music while you are meditating. For most people, playing music while meditating detracts from the meditation.

4 When you have become an experienced meditator (ie, when you have practised meditation regularly for at least several months and feel comfortable with it) you can try creating 'on the spot' mantras. To do this, you make up new mantra sounds to fit your mood of a particular day. The new sound created will not supplant your regular mantra (the latter will return to you frequently as though to an old friend) but the mantra-of-the-moment can be extremely effective in helping you cope with immediate pressures.

Commence your meditation as usual – in restful

silence with eyes closed. Do not consciously start thinking your mantra. Instead remain seated quietly until a sound comes to mind that seems to express your feelings of the moment. If you wait silently and peacefully and do not try to think of a sound, one will come to you naturally. It may be a relatively unstructured sound (such as 'Eeee-oooh') or it may take a more definite form, seeming like a word from some strange language (sounds such as 'Ahah-zamm'; 'Mahn-bee-tumm'; 'Ah-rah-remm'; 'Hah-dumm' are examples of more structured types). The combinations of sounds which can arise spontaneously are limitless. Dr Harmon S. Ephron, who devised this technique, used it for many years and stated that during this entire period never once did the same sound repeat itself.

As you practise the technique, you will find that your self-created mantras may change many times as the session proceeds. Let your self-created mantra change as many times as it wants to: this means that your inner pressures are shifting too (as a result of meditation) and that a new sound is more suitable for the present moment. You may use this method of meditating when you feel it is particularly appropriate to do so, or you may adopt it permanently.

5 Listen to the recording on Side 7, 'Enhancing Your Life With Meditation'. This recording helps you to integrate meditation into your life as a natural and life-enhancing practice.

6 Listen to the recording on Side 8, 'Timing and Renewing Your Meditation Practice'. The first part of this recording talks you through two preparatory exercises which may help to deepen your meditation practice and to make it even more meaningful.

Meditating Under Stress

Meditation can be applied during periods of heavy stress in your life to neutralize the emotional load you are carrying. Here are some suggestions:

1 Use mini-meditations liberally. These can be as short as one minute and should be scattered throughout the day. The aim is to keep bringing down the stress level before too much tension has had a chance to accumulate.

2 Schedule an extra full meditation session (or several) into your day. The correct procedure for using such extra sessions is outlined on page 50. These extra sessions do not constitute 'over meditation' if you return to your regular routine of twice (or once) a day meditation as soon as the period of stress in your life is over.

3 If you are extremely upset about something, thoughts and feelings about the problem may preoccupy your mind so that your ordinary meditation cannot compete. As a result, some people say they are unable to get benefit from meditation just when they need it the most.

   If you encounter this, try one of the following:

   a If you are already practising the basic CSM technique as taught on the instruction tape (Side 3), switch temporarily to one of the alternative forms of meditation taught on pages 80–83. These structured forms of meditation occupy your mind more fully and can be useful under stress.

      You can use this more structured form of meditation for your entire meditation session if you wish, or you can employ it during the first three or four minutes only. It may take only a few minutes of structured meditation to pull your mind away from your problems sufficiently so that you can revert to your regular method of meditating for the remainder of the meditation session.

Keep on using the structured meditation in this manner for as long as your life-stress situation continues.

b Engage in three to four minutes of deep abdominal breathing (as described on page 53) before starting your meditation session. This calms the emotions and steadies the mind so that meditation can take hold.

c Engage in several minutes of Progressive Muscle Relaxation (as described on pages 70–71) before commencing your meditation session. Quietness of body can contribute greatly to quietness of mind.

d Combine your meditation with physical exercise (as described on page 58). Walking, jogging, or swimming are particularly useful exercises to use for this purpose because they are rhythmic in nature. If you are confined indoors, walk back and forth in the largest space available – you will want to take continuous unbroken strides if possible. If you are confined to a small room, walk extremely slowly, hands lightly clasped behind your back, allowing yourself to sway from side to side as you walk in an easy rocking motion. When accompanied by rhythmic repetition of the mantra, such types of exercise can bring considerable relief from tension. The combination of meditation and exercise releases mental and physical tensions simultaneously.

e Sometimes, when you are under exceptional pressure, it may be difficult to settle into your meditation. At these times you can give yourself some extra support by meditating along with the recording on Side 8, 'Timing and Renewing Your Meditation Practice'. This recording provides two short preparatory exercises and gently guides you through your meditation. Use one or both of the relaxation exercises taught on this tape for several minutes until you experience greater calm.

Mini-Meditation Stress-Control Programme

Caution: If this programme is undertaken for health reasons, I strongly recommend the supervision by a doctor or other health professional who is familiar with the effects of profound relaxation upon medical conditions and drug therapy (see pages 84–8). Patients suffering from hypertension or diabetes, for example, may need gradual reductions in medication for these conditions while engaging in this programme.

The Format

The mini-meditation stress-control programme is both for people suffering from hypertension or other stress-related conditions and for those who work under high stress or face exceptional pressures in their daily life. The programme calls for the use of mini-meditations (mini-mediations are described in detail on Sides 6 and 7 of the recordings) as a means of bringing down tension levels on the spot without waiting for the build-up of tension that can take place over the span of a day. Momentary rises in tension level play an important role, for example, in bringing about a rise in blood pressure or other emergency responses of the body. Mini-meditations (as opposed to regular twice daily meditation) have the advantage of being able to lower tension *repeatedly* throughout the day, so that the tension does not have a chance to build to a peak level. These short meditations which interrupt the stress build-up cycle are to be used along with your two regular meditations of the day.

The Steps to Follow

The mini-meditation stress-control programme should be started only after you have been practising CSM for at least three to four weeks (or more). It should not be commenced during the adjustment period (first three weeks) because at this time you will still be getting accustomed to your regular meditation routine and will not be ready to add the short meditations.

Required Materials

You will need ruled index cards measuring approximately 3 x 5 inches: a separate card for each day of the programme. On each card, draw vertical lines, forming three columns. Leave a space for the date at the top of each card; then write in the hours of the day from the time you usually rise until you reach your usual sleep hour. Your completed card will look similar to this:

Date		
7am	*1pm*	*7pm*
8am	*2pm*	*8pm*
9am	*3pm*	*9pm*
10am	*4pm*	*10pm*
11am	*5pm*	*11pm*
12 noon	*6pm*	*12 midnight*

Procedure

First Week: Each day of the week, carry one of these cards with you wherever you go, keeping it where it can be reached easily. As you go about your regular routine, pause every hour on the hour, take out the card and make a note on it; you are writing down your 'tension score' for that hour in the appropriate square provided on the card. You may be able to set your watch to provide an hourly reminder signal.

Tension scores are estimates of your present state, on a scale of 1 to 100; with '1' indicating total relaxation (the most relaxed, 'at ease' condition you can imagine); and with '100' indicating total tension (such extreme tension that you would presumably 'explode' if you reached that level). Determine your present tension score by jotting down a number (from 1 to 100) which indicates where you are now according to your present feelings of tension or relaxation. Do this without thinking too much about it, just record the first number that comes to mind in connection with your present feelings. Do this every hour on the hour and stick to this recording procedure like clockwork during the first week.

End-of-Week Evaluation: At the end of the first week, look over your daily tension cards for that week. As you do so you may notice some interesting things about your own stress patterns. You may find, for example, that certain hours of the day or certain days of the week are particularly high-stress times for you. After a week of observing, you may also find that you are now becoming more aware of your own tension levels. This is good; it is a first step towards handling tension build-ups more effectively. Basically, we cannot begin to cope with something until we know about it.

Now, after reading over the first week's cards, ask yourself a question and give a 'snap' answer to it –

answering with the first number on the tension scale of 1 to 100 that pops into your mind. The question is:

Which score on the tension scale represents my personal Safety Level?

Think of your 'Safety Level' as an imaginary line which, if it were drawn, would fall on a spot on the scale where all scores *below* it reflected feelings of being comfortable, at ease, in control, 'together', cool, relaxed, etc – and all scores *above* it reflected feelings of tension, pressure, anger, fear, distress, discomfort, the sensation of being about to explode, etc.

In short, it would be a cut-off point dividing relaxed responses from tension-producing ones. When you have decided on your Safety Level, write it down; this level is going to have an important role to play in your work in this programme.

Second Week: During the second week of the programme prepare another seven cards and write your Safety Level at the top of each card. Proceed exactly as you did the first week; except now when you jot down your tension score at the beginning of every hour, notice how close that score is to the cut-off point which you have designated as your Safety Level. If at any time your tension score has *reached* or is *exceeding* your Safety Level, stop whatever it is you are doing *as soon as possible* (using any excuse you can to get away) and immediately take a three to five minute mini-meditation, after which, return to your regular daily activities. You will be surprised at the effectiveness of this short relaxation.

From now on, take a mini-meditation at those times when your hourly tension score reaches or exceeds your safety level.

After the Second Week: Continue with the card-checking procedure (as in the second week) until you find that you are beginning to sense – quite automatically and without having to think about it – that your tension score is exceeding your Safety Level. Soon you may find that an automatic safety signal goes off in your mind, signalling when you need to stop and take a mini-meditation. When this happens, you can dispense with the clock-checking and card-writing procedures; you are now sensitive enough to your own tension level to catch momentary rises in tension, without the assistance of the cards, and you will control them by using mini-meditations on the spot as needed.

This stress-control strategy now becomes a permanent part of your life. You will find that by using mini-meditations each time your tension score exceeds your personal Safety Level, you can manage your own stress level much more effectively.

Alternate Programme

Very busy people in high-pressured occupations are sometimes unable to follow the second week's programme exactly; they may not be able to excuse themselves every time their Safety Level has been exceeded to take an immediate mini-meditation. If this is true of you, you can still get considerable benefit from the stress-control programme by keeping the plan for the second week in mind as an ideal towards which you should strive, but in the meantime compromising by taking needed mini-meditations only when you have the opportunity to do so.

This modified strategy will help considerably in reducing tension build-up, but to keep in practice, from time to time, when it becomes possible (perhaps on a weekend or a holiday) you should follow the 'card-checking-on-the-hour' routine for a day. This will ensure your ability to recognize tension build-ups in yourself when mini-meditations may be necessary.

Renewing Your Meditation Practice

You may stop meditating for some weeks, months or even longer. This can happen for a variety of reasons and may leave you feeling out of touch with your meditation practice. If this applies to you, the recording on Side 8, 'Timing and Renewing Your Meditation Practice', may be just what you need to help re-establish your meditations. It provides two short preparatory exercises and guides you through a 10, 15, or 20 minute meditation. You can meditate using this recording until you feel comfortable to meditate on your own again.

Further Information about Your Meditation Practice

For more detailed information on the practice of CSM and how other people are using it, see Dr Carrington's book *The Book of Meditation*, the companion volume to this kit.

Alternative Methods of Meditation

Some people feel more relaxed when they have definite rules to follow while meditating. Instead of repeating the mantra 'freely' in your mind (ie letting it come and go as it wants), you may systematically link the sound to your breathing.

Here are some alternate methods that have proven most satisfactory.

Method Number 1

Dr Herbert Benson of Harvard Medical School, a leading meditation researcher, developed this method of creating the 'relaxation response':

1 Sit quietly in a comfortable position.

2 Close your eyes.

3 Deeply relax all your muscles, beginning at your feet and progressing up to your face (see Progressive Muscle Relaxation, page 70). Allow them to stay relaxed.

4 Breathe through your nose. Become aware of your breathing. As you breathe out, say the word 'ONE', silently to yourself. For example, breathe IN . . . OUT, 'ONE'; IN . . . OUT, 'ONE'; etc. Breathe easily and naturally.

5 Continue meditating in this manner for the amount of time suggested on the CSM tapes and workbook. Use the same general instructions for practising meditation as you would if you were continuing with the technique as you learned it from the tape. When you finish, sit quietly for several minutes, at first with your eyes closed and later with your eyes opened.

6 Do not worry about whether you are successful in achieving a deep level of relaxation. Maintain a passive attitude and permit relaxation to occur at its own pace. When distracting thoughts occur, try to ignore them by not dwelling upon them – simply say to yourself something akin to 'oh, well', and return to repeating 'one'. With practice, the response should come with little effort.[4] If you wish, you can make up a suitable mantra of your own, or substitute one of the mantras on page 10 or use a short prayer or religious phrase in place of the word 'one'.

Method Number 2

This form of breathing meditation was developed by Dr Robert Woolfolk of the Department of Psychology at Rutgers University:

[4]From *The Relaxation Response,* by Herbert Benson, MD. © Copyright 1975 by William Morrow & Co., Inc. Courtesy of the publisher. Adapted.

Take a single, slow, deep breath, thinking to yourself the word 'in' as you breathe in, and 'out' as you breathe out. Do not intentionally influence your breathing but let it go its own way, fast or slow, shallow or deep, whatever way it wishes. As you do so, just think to yourself 'in' on every in-breath and 'out' on every out-breath.

When doing this breathing meditation, try to extend the sound you are repeating in your mind so that at all points during meditation you are either thinking 'in . . . n . . . n . . . n . . .' or 'ouuuuuuuut . . .' in long, easy sounds. If the word 'out' sounds too abrupt because it ends in 't' and this is distracting (it is for some people), you can substitute the syllable 'ah' for the word 'out' – saying 'in' as you breathe in and 'ah' as you breathe out.

Another option is to use one of the two-syllable mantras listed on page 10, or make up a suitable two-syllable mantra of your own, always linking the first syllable with the in-breath and the second with the out-breath.

When you finish, sit quietly for several minutes, at first with your eyes closed and later with your eyes open.

With respect to all other aspects of your meditation routine, refer to the instructions given on the CSM tapes and in this workbook.

Method Number 3

This form of breathing meditation was developed by psychologist Dr Brad Wilson:

> Begin by observing your breathing without trying to influence it, then start counting to four, linking each separate number with an out-breath. You will think 'one' on the first out-breath, 'two' on the second out-breath, 'three' on the third, 'four' on the fourth, and then start over again. Continue in this manner for a total of about three minutes, then stop.

This mini-meditation can be done as many times a day as you wish providing your total meditation time for the day does not add up to more than 40–45 minutes. While doing it you can be sitting, standing, or moving about. You can be thinking about anything you want, feeling anything you want, or having any kind of fantasy. If you lose count, come back to the task easily and without self-blame and begin again with the count of 'one'.

With respect to all other aspects of your meditation routine, refer to the instructions given on the CSM tapes and in this workbook.

Method Number 4

You may prefer not to repeat any sound in your mind but remain inwardly silent while meditating on your breath. Focus your attention on one area involved in the breathing process, such as the delicate sensation of the breath passing in and out through your nostrils or the rise and fall of your abdomen with each in-breath and out-breath. While doing this, do not try to influence your breathing in any manner. When your mind wanders, simply return to the process of watching your breath without forcing.

When you finish, sit quietly for several minutes, at first with your eyes closed and later with your eyes open.

With respect to all other aspects of your meditation routine, refer to the instructions given on the CSM tapes and in this workbook.

I suggest that you try each one of the above forms of meditation before selecting the one that feels best to you. After that, continue listening to your remaining CSM tapes and read the workbook, in the order set out in 'Your Programme for This Course', at the beginning of this workbook. From now on, where the instructions tell you to 'let your mantra come and go as it wishes' (or allow it to disappear and reappear freely) you will substitute the alternate instructions given above.

Information Sheet for Doctors
Re: Clinically Standardized Meditation (CSM)

The clinical value of meditation techniques when used as adjuncts to standard medical treatment has been confirmed in a large number of studies.[1,2,3,4,5] Use of meditation has been associated with increased rate of autonomic recovery from laboratory-induced stressful events;[3,6] decreased blood pressure in both pharmacologically treated and untreated hypertensive patients[7,8,9] and reduction in premature ventricular contractions in patients with stable ischaemic heart disease.[10] It has been used in the treatment of coronary artery disease;[11] angina pectoris;[12] insomnia;[13] addictive behaviour;[14,15,16] asthma;[17] epilepsy;[18] hypercholesterolemia;[19] diabetes;[20] psoriasis;[21] and fibromyalgia,[22] among other medical conditions.

This method, Clinically Standardized Meditation or CSM, was developed for patient populations and later adapted for the general population. The CSM method emphasizes adjustment of the technique to suit individual needs, with trainees learning to self-regulate their meditation. Physicians supervising the use of CSM should note the following:

Use with Hypertension. Research shows meditation to be generally useful in helping to reduce high blood pressure[7,8,9] but an occasional case has been reported of a hypertensive patient undergoing a form of deep-relaxation therapy who has shown a paradoxical increase in diastolic and systolic blood pressure after commencing the relaxation training.[2] While such paradoxical reactions have not been noted in any persons practising CSM, in view of their occasional occurrence with other forms of relaxation training recommend that for hypertensives the effects of meditation practice on the patient's blood pressure be determined at regular intervals during the first 90 days of meditation practice. If meditation is found to cause a significant increase in blood pressure, the practice should be discontinued.

Use with Diabetes. In diabetic patients, training in deep relaxation sometimes leads to reduced insulin requirements and to hypoglycaemia.[20,24] Frequent monitoring of urinary glucose levels and instructions to the patient to keep a readily absorbable supply of glucose in reach at all times are therefore recommended for diabetic patients practising all relaxation methods, including CSM.

Use with Thyroidectomized Patients. Deep relaxation achieved through thermal and EMG feedback has been reported to have caused a recurrence of symptoms typical of hyperthyroidism in a thyroidectomized patient on replacement therapy.[25] A similar reaction has been reported with one of the thyroidectomized patients who learned CSM. It is therefore recommended that thyroidectomized patients start their training in CSM with very short periods of meditation, meditating no more than three minutes at one time, two to three times daily. This brief exposure to meditation should be continued for the first two weeks of meditation practice with the patient's physical condition monitored during that time. If symptoms reminiscent of hyperthyroidism appear, meditation should be discontinued. If the patient adjusts comfortably to the experience of meditating during the first two weeks, then he or she can gradually increase the meditation time, doing so by once each week adding two minutes to the total time spent in each meditation session. If the patient remains asymptomatic, he or she can gradually increase meditation time up to a maximum of two 20-minute sessions per day.

Effect on Medication. Meditation may enhance the action of certain drugs in certain patients.[26] Requirements for anti-anxiety and anti-depressive as well as anti-hypertensive and thyroid-regulating medications should therefore be monitored in patients who are practising CSM. Sometimes the continued practice of meditation may permit a desirable low dosage treatment over more prolonged periods and occasionally permit the discontinuance of drug therapy altogether.[7]

Doctor Support. The doctor's support of his or her patients' efforts to employ self-help techniques such as meditation can be of great assistance in augmenting compliance with the technique and subsequent benefits. Hypertensive patients in particular appear to benefit from such continued encouragement.

References

1 Jevning, R, Wallace, R K, Beidebach, M, 'The Physiology of Meditation: A Wakeful Hypometabolic Integrated Response', *Neuroscience and Biobehavioral Reviews*, 16 (3): 415–424, 1992

2 Benson, H, Marzetta, B R, and Rosner, B A, 'Decreased Systolic Blood Pressure in Hypertensive Subjects Who Practised Meditation,' *Journal of Clinical Investigation*, 52: 8a, 1973

3 Goleman, D J and Schwartz, G E, 'Meditation as an Intervention in Stress Reactivity,' *Journal of Consulting and Clinical Psychology*, 44: 456–466, 1976

4 Carrington, P, 'Modern Forms of Meditation' in Lehrer, P M and Woolfolk, R L (eds), *Principles and Practice of Stress Management (2nd Edition)*, New York: Guilford Press, 1993, 139–168

5 Benson, H, *The Relaxation Response*, New York: Morrow, 1975

6 Daniels, D, cited in P Carrington, *Freedom in Meditation*, Anchor Press/Doubleday. 1977, 60–61

7 Shapiro, A P et al, 'Behavioural Methods in the Treatment of Hypertension,' *Annals of Internal Medicine*, 86: 626–636, 1977

8 Benson, H, 'Systemic Hypertension and the Relaxation Response', *New England Journal of Medicine*, 296: 1152–1156, 1977

9 Schneider, R H, Staggers, F, Alexander, C N, et al, 'A Randomized Controlled Trial of Stress Reduction for Hypertension in Older African Americans', *Hypertension*, 26(5): 820–827, 1995

10 Benson, H, Alexander, S, and Feldman, C L, 'Decreased Premature Ventricular Contractions Through the Use of the Relaxation Response in Patients with Stable Ischaemic Heart Disease', *Lancet*, 2: 380, 1975

11 Zamarra, J W, Schneider, R H, Besseghini, I, et al, 'Usefulness of the Transcendental Meditation Program in the Treatment of Patients with Coronary Artery Disease', *American Journal of Cardiology*, 77(10): 867–870, 1996

12 Zamarra, J W, Besseghini, I, and Wittenberg, S, 'The Effects of the Transcendental Meditation Program on the Exercise Performance of Patients with Angina Pectoris', In D W Orme-Johnson & J T Farrow (eds), *Scientific Research on the Transcendental Meditation Program: Collected Papers:* Vol. 1, Livingston Manor, NY: Maharishi European Research Press, 1978, 331–334

13 Woolfolk, R L, Carr-Kaffashan, K, Lehrer, P M, et al, 'Meditation Training as a Treatment for Insomnia', *Behaviour Therapy* 7: 359–365, 1976

14 Shafii, M, Lavely, R A and Jaffe, R D, 'Meditation and the Prevention of Alcohol Abuse', *American Journal of Psychiatry*, 132: 942–945, 1975

15 Royer, A, 'The Role of the Transcendental Meditation Program in Promoting Smoking Cessation: A Longitudinal Study', *Alcoholism Treatment Quarterly*, Vol. II (1–2): 221–239, 1994

16 Alexander, C N, Robinson, P, and Rainforth, M, 'Treating and Preventing Alcohol, Nicotine, and Drug Abuse Through Transcendental Meditation: A Review and Statistical Meta-Analysis of 19 Studies', *Alcoholism Treatment Quarterly*, Vol. II (1–2): 13–87, 1994

17 Wilson, A F, Honsberger, R, Chiu, I T, et al, 'Transcendental Meditation and Asthma', *Respiration*, 32: 74–80, 1975

18 Deepak, K K, Manchananda, S K, and Maheswari, M C, 'Meditation Improves Clinicoelectroencephalographic Measures in Drug-Resistant Epileptics', *Biofeedback and Self-Regulation*, 19 (1): 25–40, 1994

19 Cooper, M J and Aygen, M M, 'A Relaxation Technique in the Management of Hypercholesterolemia', *Journal of Human Stress*, 5: 24–27, 1979

20 Heriberto, C, 'The Effects of Clinically Standardized Meditation (CSM) on Type II Diabetics', unpublished doctoral dissertation, Adelphi University, Institute of Advanced Studies, 1988

21 Gaston, L., 'Efficacy of Imagery and Meditation Techniques in Treating Psoriasis', *Imagination, Cognition and Personality*, 8 (1): 25–38, 1988

22 Kaplan, K H, Goldenberg, D L, and Galvin-Nadeau, M, 'The Impact of a Meditation-Based Stress Reduction Program on Fibromyalgia', *General Hospital Psychiatry*, 15 (5): 284–289, 1993

23 Luthe, W and Schultz, J H, *Autogenic Therapy*, Vols. I–VI, New York: Grune and Stratton, 1969

24 Fowler, J E, Budzynski, T H, and Van den Berg, R L, 'Effects of an EMG Biofeedback Relaxation Programme on the Control of Diabetes: A Case Study', *Biofeedback and Self-Regulation*, 1: 105–112, 1976

25 Wesch, J E, Clinical Comments Section, *Newsletter of the Biofeedback Society*, 5 (3), July 1977

26 Patel, C H, 'Yoga and Biofeedback in the Management of Hypertension', *Lancet*, 2: 1053–1055, 1973

30-WEEK DAILY MEDITATION CHECKLIST

Instructions: Record each meditation by colouring in the appropriate square with pen or pencil. Colour until the square is filled. Research shows that filling in squares completely is a good way of training yourself into new habits.

Week 1	Mon	Tues	Wed	Thur	Fri	Sat	Sun
morning							
evening							
Week 2	Mon	Tues	Wed	Thur	Fri	Sat	Sun
morning							
evening							
Week 3	Mon	Tues	Wed	Thur	Fri	Sat	Sun
morning							
evening							
Week 4	Mon	Tues	Wed	Thur	Fri	Sat	Sun
morning							
evening							
Week 5	Mon	Tues	Wed	Thur	Fri	Sat	Sun
morning							
evening							
Week 6	Mon	Tues	Wed	Thur	Fri	Sat	Sun
morning							
evening							
Week 7	Mon	Tues	Wed	Thur	Fri	Sat	Sun
morning							
evening							

Week 8	Mon	Tues	Wed	Thur	Fri	Sat	Sun
morning							
evening							
Week 9	Mon	Tues	Wed	Thur	Fri	Sat	Sun
morning							
evening							
Week 10	Mon	Tues	Wed	Thur	Fri	Sat	Sun
morning							
evening							
Week 11	Mon	Tues	Wed	Thur	Fri	Sat	Sun
morning							
evening							
Week 12	Mon	Tues	Wed	Thur	Fri	Sat	Sun
morning							
evening							
Week 13	Mon	Tues	Wed	Thur	Fri	Sat	Sun
morning							
evening							
Week 14	Mon	Tues	Wed	Thur	Fri	Sat	Sun
morning							
evening							
Week 15	Mon	Tues	Wed	Thur	Fri	Sat	Sun
morning							
evening							
Week 16	Mon	Tues	Wed	Thur	Fri	Sat	Sun
morning							
evening							
Week 17	Mon	Tues	Wed	Thur	Fri	Sat	Sun
morning							
evening							
Week 18	Mon	Tues	Wed	Thur	Fri	Sat	Sun
morning							
evening							
Week 19	Mon	Tues	Wed	Thur	Fri	Sat	Sun
morning							
evening							
Week 20	Mon	Tues	Wed	Thur	Fri	Sat	Sun
morning							
evening							
Week 21	Mon	Tues	Wed	Thur	Fri	Sat	Sun
morning							
evening							

Week 22	Mon	Tues	Wed	Thur	Fri	Sat	Sun
morning							
evening							
Week 23	Mon	Tues	Wed	Thur	Fri	Sat	Sun
morning							
evening							
Week 24	Mon	Tues	Wed	Thur	Fri	Sat	Sun
morning							
evening							
Week 25	Mon	Tues	Wed	Thur	Fri	Sat	Sun
morning							
evening							
Week 26	Mon	Tues	Wed	Thur	Fri	Sat	Sun
morning							
evening							
Week 27	Mon	Tues	Wed	Thur	Fri	Sat	Sun
morning							
evening							
Week 28	Mon	Tues	Wed	Thur	Fri	Sat	Sun
morning							
evening							
Week 29	Mon	Tues	Wed	Thur	Fri	Sat	Sun
morning							
evening							
Week 30	Mon	Tues	Wed	Thur	Fri	Sat	Sun
morning							
evening							

Appendix

Room Preparations

INDEX

OTHER AUDIO TAPES & BOOKS BY DR CARRINGTON

Health care providers who wish to use CSM as a clinical or research tool can obtain a CSM INSTRUCTOR'S KIT which will enable them to supervise the use of this method for their patients or trainees. The kit contains clinical lectures on the use of CSM with varied personality and health problems (on three audio tapes) and an Instructor's Manual. To obtain information, contact the following centres in the UK or USA:

UNITED KINGDOM: Learning for Life Ltd, The Coach House, Chinewood Manor, 32 Manor Road, Bournemouth, BH1 3EZ, UK. Phone/fax#: 01202 390008 (international +44 1202 390008).

UNITED STATES: Pace Educational Systems, Inc,
61 Kingsley Road, Kendall Park, NJ 08824, USA.
Toll-free phone#: 1-800-297-9897. Fax#: 732-297-0778.

Information on other tapes and books by Dr Carrington is also available from the above sources.

CSM has considerable value when used within organizational settings

For information about introducing CSM into:

- Commercial organizations
- Public authorities
- Stress and lifestyle management courses
- Staff welfare and development programmes
- Medical settings
- Educational establishments

Contact: Learning for Life Ltd or Pace Educational Systems, Inc.